Plant Wisdom

Friends, Allies and Helpers in Your Garden

Mellie Uyldert

Originally translated from the Dutch by H. A. Smith

First published in Holland as *Plantenzielen*
© De Driehoek, Amsterdam

First English edition published 1980 by Thorsons Publishers Ltd

Second English edition published 1996 by Altea Publishing,
Parkmount House, 10 St Leonards Road,
Forres IV36 0DW, Scotland

ISBN 0 9524555 3 6

British Library Cataloguing-in-Publication Data. A catalogue record
for this book is available from the British Library.

Layout and setting by Altea Publishing.
Cover photo by Findhorn Foundation Visual Arts
Printed and bound by Guernsey Press Ltd.

Contents

Introduction

Recent years have seen a growing desire for a more natural way of life. A great many people are yearning for a return to the time when there was a happier relationship between humans, animals and plants, as they become increasingly disgusted by our modern farming methods. This reaction perhaps represents a stirring of our long-stifled primeval instincts. We were born to coexist with other life on this planet, and there are esoteric overtones to the trend towards more and more of us getting out into our gardens or allotments to grow natural food the natural way.

But do we really need to bludgeon our plots of land into military order to achieve the results we seek? Why not leave it to nature? If you forget the weeding, and simply leave the ground fallow, the following spring will bring an assortment of plants that like your soil and that like you. Of all the millions of seeds scattered by the wind, the ones that fall and germinate in your garden will be precisely those that have the same vibrations as the place in which you live — and as yourself. Soil, water, air, animals, plants and human beings which have an affinity as types will find each other and form a community that will serve, feed and restore itself.

Your garden is your mirror. In it, you can see your own pattern. If, for example, it is full of daisies, couch and sorrel, this means that your soil is acid and that your blood perhaps also tends to acidity. These plants will neutralise the soil by introducing chalk into it. Plants are great alchemists: they manufacture substances that the soil in which they grow does not contain. By eating these plants (for instance, by boiling down the root stocks of couch as tea or decorating your salads with daisies) you can de-acidify your blood and so avoid sciatica, lumbago and rheumatism.

Nature therefore looks after us. Even before we know that we are ill, the appropriate medicinal herb will be growing in our garden — if only we do not weed it out!

It is conceit that spoils it all for us. Paradise is all around us, waiting to be re-created. But we are muddleheaded Adams and Eves. We think that nature is not quite up to scratch and that we can improve on it. And so we create unnatural fields of only one crop, which attracts swarms of insects, or we cultivate immaculate lawns with much labour and expensive machinery and without a single dandelion to be seen. And when all the back-breaking work is done we sit on our terraces and survey our handiwork, crippled by the gallstones that the leaves of a dandelion could have prevented.

Perhaps one day our earth will once again become the paradise it originally was — when we learn to apply a deep knowledge of plants to our way of life.

"Consider the lilies of the field, how they grow; they toil not, neither do they spin: And yet I say unto you, that even Solomon in all his glory was not arrayed like one of these."

PART 1
Plants and Humans

1. Let Nature Do the Gardening

Yes, a garden is a pleasant place, but you must be at it all summer, whether it is a flower or a kitchen garden, always composting, weeding, pruning and picking, and then sowing or planting.

But this is only if you insist on having a garden with immaculate borders and straight rows of vegetables and filled with all the latest plants from the nursery. Though many of these plants do not really belong in our climate, with the aid of cold frames and cloches and doses of artificial fertilisers we can still produce something to be proud of.

But there is another way. It needs, however, a different attitude of mind. It succeeds only if we no longer try to bend nature to our own whims but are prepared to learn from it; if we can keep our hands to ourselves and wait to see how nature does it — what plants it allows to grow on what soil with that intrinsic wisdom that we only come to appreciate with time.

Natural Gardening

Why do we spend so much money and trouble on fertilisers? How does Mother Nature go to work in this respect?

Well, she understands the art of making new from old. She is the greatest of alchemists. She converts one substance to another, all by herself, with the aid of weather and climate. When, in the autumn, the plants have concentrated all their strength in seeds and lose the shape they have built up earlier in the summer, the leaves and stalks gradually decay into earth. The following spring, the germinating seeds use this as their nourishment, and the circle is completed. Mother Earth does not rake, but allows the laws of nature to work.

Nor does Mother Nature water or spray. The rain provides

humidity and in a dry period the plants have only to stretch out their roots to the ground water, which gives them strength. Weeds do not die, we say. No, they are strong because they are not molly-coddled like our cultivated plants. Moreover, nature always provides the soil with a green cover which prevents it from drying out. It abhors a vacuum and immediately provides a carpet for bare patches. In the kitchen garden, fresh chickweed immediately covers empty beds. So do we have to weed again? Not really. Eat this tasty salad for a while; it comes back immediately and costs you nothing.

Nor does nature dig. The earthworms do this, keeping the soil friable and digging passageways by eating earth. They excrete the earth they digest, but don't ingest, as an improved kind of loam, loose and predigested for plants.

Insects

And what does nature do against harmful insects? For this, it has provided birds which devour enormous quantities of insects — in your garden, too, if only you do not cut down the trees and shrubs in which they have to live. Nature is a great harmonious whole in which each plant and each animal has a function benefiting the whole. The ladybird eats the aphids on the plants. Snails eat the moss on the trunks of the fruit trees. Moles and worms keep the earth friable. Wild animals — hedgehogs, rabbits, squirrels — add their manure to the ground. Honeybees and bumblebees fertilise your fruit trees and bushes.

Plagues of insects do not occur in the natural scheme. Nature is not so stupid as to install single cultures — endless fields planted with one crop only, in which so-called weeds are always diligently rooted out or eradicated with poison. As if this poison does not at the same time ruin the ground as a whole! If a generation of caterpillars finds a field full of tasty cabbages they eat and eat until everything is bare. But if the cabbage grows next to a sage bush which, with its strong smell, repels the caterpillar, we shall not have such catastrophes. Nature always creates a harmony of plants that complement each other. So plagues are avoided and the composition of the ground is kept in balance. One plant type produces what another lacks. So-called weeds in the field make the grain more tasty, more nourishing and stronger.

Nature's Purpose

Do not pull out what nature has sown: she has a purpose in providing it. The sorrel which causes you so much trouble was intended to add chalk to the soil (so you do not then have to buy lime). Stinging nettles, too, improve your ground and are also fine vegetables. Even couch grass, so disliked because of its endless root stocks, is good for your soil and wherever it grows new growth does particularly well. Harvest the couch roots, dry them and drink their tea. This will help free you from rheumatism. Just look: when your seeds come up, you will often find a sprout of couch close to a newly germinated plant. Tearing it out angrily would be ungracious because the rhizome has kept this spot of earth friable for the tender young root.

Nature does not set its sights on the plant kingdom alone. It lets all the natural kingdoms cooperate. The wild animals manure the ground, while the trees with their roots retain the rain water which produces the shady streams where the animals come to drink. The bird nests in the branches of the tree, the rabbit makes its burrow between its roots. The bees fertilise the flowers while collecting their nectar. The various kingdoms must keep contact. Human, animal, plant and stone, cloud and wind, sun, moon and star all need each other and help each other, and they also learn from one another.

The butterflies of the broom, the bean and vetchling imitate the shape of the butterfly which visits them because they too want to have wings and flutter about freely. That is why, in collaboration with the bacteria, they create so much albumen in the earth — in order to have something of the same life of the senses as do animals.

However, you will say, by crossing and grafting, humankind has obtained many new varieties which serve us as food or to beautify our lives. Of course, but nature also produces new plants and new animals and not merely by crossing sorts. Nature provides an endless kingdom and variation of forms. Now and again a new form occurs and another dies out. This often happens in conjunction with the stars. Each cosmic force wishes to display itself in its own form on other heavenly bodies wherever possible. A far-off star therefore causes its own type of persons, animals, plants and stones to appear on Earth. A star originates from a condensing fog, lives, grows, hardens and finally dissolves, just like other living beings. The race that represented it on Earth then ceases to have its pattern strengthened by it and dies out. If a new star begins to radiate, then a new form of life occurs on Earth, in each kingdom of nature. In this way, everything on Earth is born from the cosmos and in time goes back to it.

2. Your Own Herb in Your Own Garden

Mother Nature plants for us precisely what we need. This is based on natural law. A particular point in the earth's crust contains certain substances in a specific relationship and this produces a vibration to which a corresponding vibration answers from the universe. The atmosphere lying between them then also vibrates sympathetically. This applies to ground water and to plants, animals and people, who are attracted to this as types by the law of the attraction of like things. It is not, therefore, in any way coincidental that certain wild plants germinate and thrive in a certain spot. Thousands of seeds are carried by the wind, but only those that are drawn towards the soil at that spot by their own vibration reach the ground there and germinate in due course. A vibration of this kind is a characteristic of an axis which may be a very little or quite greatly affected by the vibration in the same way as two opposing signs of the zodiac form an axis. In this way, the least can attract the most, and we call this the attraction of opposites. On this principle homoeopathy too is based.

Correspondences

What grows in your garden, therefore, is related to you. People are drawn to the spot where they should be, although they may provide all kinds of rational arguments for living there. According to the laws, we cannot at any time be elsewhere than where we are. The same cosmic scheme therefore determines the presence of both herb and human. If an illness is busy developing unnoticed in the human body, the appropriate medicinal herb will germinate in the garden. And when we say "Oh, what an odd plant has come up here!" the illness is manifested. If only people knew the connection, they would quickly cure themselves. But because we no longer consult our inborn knowledge and our instinct, the curative herb remains unrecognised and unpicked and the illness seeks a remedy by the long detour of the intellect.

It is noteworthy that the plant will disappear again when it is no longer required as a medicine, since the cause of both — herb and illness — disappears. One example out of thousands: the land surrounding newly-built old people's flats in Holland had been so stirred up by the builders that nothing would grow there any more. Before anything had been done in the way of putting down a garden, a mass of marigolds appeared, which do not grow wild in Holland — that was remarkable in itself. Of the old people who had come to live in the building, three had cancer. Now, marigold is a traditional remedy against cancer. But no one knew that. The following spring, and the next, the marigolds again appeared until first the one, then the second and then the third cancer patient had passed on. The spring after the latter had died, quite suddenly no marigolds appeared. Although it stood to reason that the plants should have again sown themselves in ground which so obviously suited them, the scheme had been completed, for human and plant alike.

Wild plants that may be needed somewhere cannot be eradicated. A mother complained that in her little garden shepherd's purse would appear again and again, grow enormously large and reappear the next year, however much they tried to root it out. "What good does it do?" she asked. Answer: it prevents bleeding, particularly nosebleeds. Even a bunch of shepherd's purse just hung around the neck will help. As it happened, it seems that at the time her son suffered from recurring nosebleeds, which baffled the doctor. Alas, they did not know the power of the herb which was standing there ready to help!

More Examples

We have seen how, in the garden of a person who always had

trouble with her bronchial passages, lungwort would appear each year of its own accord. Just rubbing its hairy leaves against the chest can help, and its tea can also be drunk. After many years of trouble, the patient moved house and took the lungwort plants with her, and they were given a place in the new garden. In the new house, the patient no longer suffered from asthma and bronchitis and the next year the lungwort had similarly disappeared. It was no longer required.

There was a person who, for years, was afflicted with diarrhoea. In the garden, the herb bennet grew abundantly — the best intestinal tonic there is, though she did not know it. When, much later, she learned the secret and began to take tincture of the root, diarrhoea and bleeding disappeared, as did the bennet the next year.

A person living not far from the Leiden University botanical gardens had a splendid hogweed appear in her garden, a plant which really feels more at home in an old park or wood than in a city garden. To be sure, people said, it had blown in from the botanical gardens. Her son began to suffer from epileptic fits. A friend who consulted a herbalist for advice was informed that hogweed is the specific against epilepsy.

A woman saw an unusual plant appear by her kitchen doorstep. It appeared to be a butterbur, a medicament against cancer. A while later, she was found to have this disease.

Someone asked, "How can it be that there is such an abundance of camomile in my garden?" "Do you happen to suffer from nerves?" "Oh yes, it stops me sleeping." "Then take a cup of soothing camomile tea daily!"

A woman who thought she was in perfect health always found her kitchen garden full of Solomon's Seal. Unexpectedly, her doctor diagnosed diabetes. Had she but drunk tea of Solomon's Seal, the complaint would have been dealt with at the outset.

A Gemini, always intellectually very active, had a garden full of orach which she ate with pleasure. Later, she discovered in a book that this plant contains quicksilver, the Gemini metal needed for mental activity.

A young man who suffered from numbness of the fingers and cold feet, and therefore had poor blood circulation, had yarrow in his garden, which with its extremely finely divided leaves indicates a correspondence with the human capillaries. Anaemic people and those deficient in calcium have a lot of nettles in their gardens. If only they would eat plenty of them!

So, Mother Nature looks after humans and animals. The cat eats grass when it feels unwell and so each animal seeks out the herb it needs. Only humankind has stopped listening to the voice of instinct.

3. Do Plants Have Feelings?

People who talk to their indoor plants have been laughed at by others until quite recently. But scientific tests have shown that these people were right. Plants have a soul and this is clear to those who love them.

The tests were made with the aid of a lie detector, an electrical apparatus with a pointer which describes a curve on a sheet of paper in line with the vibrations that it records. Fastened to a person who is being questioned, for example during court proceedings, it describes a straight line as long as the person is speaking the truth but will suddenly waver when a lie is told. In fact, the truth that a person knows in his or her heart normally flows along in the electrical nerve stream through to the brain but is then violated, resulting in stagnation and over-compensation.

A detector of this kind was fastened to a plant and its vibration field, life pattern or 'L field' was recorded. When the plant was pricked, i.e. when pain was inflicted, the detector reacted violently. And when pain was inflicted on a second plant in the same room, the first reacted just as violently out of sympathy. Finally, in the same room, a live shrimp was thrown into boiling water, whereupon the plant shook indignantly.

The Sensitivity of Plants

Sensitive people have long known that plants do better if they are given a friendly word or touched or if the hand is held over them for a moment each day (with good intentions) so that love is radiated out to them. And a grateful plant will show its love: the plant lover will know of many examples — how, as he walks through his rose garden, the scent of roses will suddenly waft towards him, and how certain kinds of plants, related to him and linked to him by affinity, spring up by themselves in a row along his garden path or on either side of his front door. This has been my own experience with a birch tree, which I dearly love. My ground-floor has three pairs of french windows. Small birches have sprouted on either side of each, and even between the stones of the steps. And there is one by the kitchen door which is not bothered by the fact that the door opens and closes over the top of him.

An American expert in the lie detector field — he prefers to call them 'polygraphs' — is Cleve Backster of New York. He began his tests by attaching an instrument of this kind to a plant when he was about to water it, to see whether the electrical resistance in the leaf might change as the water rose from root to leaf. To his amazement, he saw a curve appear equal to that which records the emotions in a human. He then made further tests. While the device was still fastened to the plant he thought he would burn one of its leaves. Immediately, the plant showed its fear by violent jumps of the needle. It could also read his thoughts!

Even at a distance, the plant, which was cared for by him daily and whose vibration field was accordingly linked to his, began to react to what he did or how he felt. In the same way that a dog begins to bark and wag its tail as soon as its owner is on his way along the street, even though still out of sight, so the plant reacted: when Backster turned into his street, the plant showed its joy by greater emotional fluctuation of the needle, which he checked by means of a stop-watch. When, once, he was nearly run over by a car, the plant showed its fright at the same moment. So everything lives our lives with us.

On another occasion, Backster had six friends draw lots for a task. In the room where the two plants were standing, they opened up their ballot papers and the one who was given the task carried it out after everyone had left. This was to destroy one of the plants. He then left the room. The remaining plant was connected up to the polygraph. Subsequently, the six individuals entered one after the other. The apparatus reacted only to the murderer of the other plant! The remaining plant recognised his vibration as that of the murderer.

Once, Cleve Backster allowed a friend into his room while the plant was connected up and asked him in what year he was born. The friend gave an incorrect year and the plant immediately caused the needle to jerk in indignation. This caused the psychiatrist Dr A.H. Esser to question a woman, together with two assistants, in the presence of a philodendron, a plant that she tended daily. A polygraph was attached to the plant and they began to ask the woman questions to which she sometimes gave correct and sometimes incorrect answers. The plant showed which were incorrect.

Bioplasmas

When two living beings, a human and a plant, or an animal and a human, coincide with each other, their vibration fields or life patterns (bioplasmas) combine into one. What from then on moves or affects the one will at the same time also affect the other. After all, a mother always knows when something happens to her child. Sensitive people are sometimes suddenly and irresistibly impelled to a strange address and it turns out that they have arrived there just at the right moment to solve a problem. One being calls out to another for help — consciously or unconsciously.

What do grass plants not have to suffer when we mow and roll our lawns? There are people who believe they can hear the whole lawn screaming. And all because we think that the lawn must be mown because long grass, when it is wet, is unsuitable for people to walk or sit on. Yet — now that public reactions are changing — the seed merchants have suddenly come up with the information that there are grass types that stay short and that are speckled with small flowers like the real spring pasture of the past.

Music

Plants are also sensitive to music. After that was discovered, loudspeakers were placed in the endless, monotonous cornfields of Canada to broadcast music for the grain throughout the days of summer. It has been proved that grain particularly appreciates classical music; it grows faster, becomes more abundant and forms more seed. Modern music, on the other hand, tends to have the opposite effect.

Indoor plants also do particularly well in rooms where fine

piano playing is regularly to be heard. This is not to say that plants hear in the same way that people do. They absorb the vibrations of the music into their own vibration fields and in this way become subject to its influence. Sick people can also be cured with suitable music, whether it is their soul or their body which is sick. And even sound that cannot be heard, because the vibrations are too coarse or too fine for the human ear, has its effect on the vibration field that receives it. In this way, certain complaints are cured by ultra-short-wave sound.

To what extent a plant can be conscious of the pain or sorrow done to it, we do not yet know. It evidently has a kind of con-sciousness similar to that of human beings when they are dream-ing. There are a great many degrees of consciousness and these are slowly being discovered by science (though sensitive people have always known of them). Perhaps people will after all take some more interest in the life around them which is so rich in surprises — in the way that life on Earth is a sequence of surprises to the very small child. Experiencing how everything is connected with everything else redeems us from our needless loneliness.

4. Plants Living Together

In the same way that plants have feelings, so they form friendships and enmities amongst themselves. What is more, these can be far more intense than those amongst people, since a plant cannot avoid its neighbour. A person can walk away from a partner to whom she is unsuited but the poor plant is nailed to the spot by its roots. If it stands next to another plant which through its size or height deprives it of sunlight, it can still try and outgrow it, although more often than not it does not succeed. But if the scent and radiation of its neighbour are detrimental to it, it can do no more than turn aside a little, fall ill and die.

Sometimes, we have a plant in our room or garden that just fails to make the grade. We give it water, light, the correct temperature, fertiliser and a friendly word now and again — yet it still is not happy, and it pines and finally dies. How inadequate we then feel as a foolish person who was not even able to understand the plant's complaint. What was it that did not suit it? Perhaps we shall never know. Let us at least try, by careful observation, to discover the likes of the various kinds of plants.

There are, of course, people who have 'green fingers', with whom all plants thrive. But for most people the fact is that some plants thrive with them and other kinds do not. It is a question of affinity, which attracts, or of rejection through too great a dissimilarity.

Natural Dislikes

Generally speaking, plants also act like this amongst each other. There are flowers that you must not place together in a vase — for instance, tulips and daffodils are nice to look at but the daffodils then quickly fade as they do not like the proud tulips. Nor do tulips combine any better with lilac; the lilac will quickly drop. Roses cannot bear carnations or mignonettes. Lilies-of-the-valley are charming and fill the whole room with their scent. But other flowers cannot survive next to them. If you make up a colourful summer bouquet, be sure not to include poppies or monk's hood; they kill the other flowers. The poppy will also then expire itself.

From a purely chemical point of view, these phenomena are due to substances which one plant forms and deposits and the other takes up. However, on the spiritual plane this is accompanied by vibrations which are transmitted and received. Growers have discovered from experience what plants do well together and which cannot get on. Roses, for example, are princely flowers which need space around themselves and will certainly suffer no humble plant population in their presence. Nonetheless, they give off more scent if placed in the company of onions and garlic! They also welcome parsley and lupins.

The vine will turn up its fine nose to cabbage and does not like the bayleaf either. But it has no objection to the elm and poppy. The olive and the oak are too strong and different in their personalities to put up with each other. Planted next to one another by humans, they bend their branches in opposite directions. On the other hand, the olive loves the myrtle and the fig tree.

On the heath, birch and fir seek each other's company, forming a community together with the erica and toadstools in which they all do well. If people chop down the firs, the heath can no longer maintain itself and is chased off by grass, and the toadstools disappear. Under the brown beeches, nothing else will grow, perhaps because, so it is said, they soak up all the evil from their surroundings.

The walnut and oak cannot stand each other, nor can blackthorn and may. In this case, through affinity, the one plant considers the other to be impure. Thus we often find that the various varieties or genera of the same species are incompatible: the stronger chokes out the weaker. For example, the *rhododendron alpinum* and the *rhododendron hirsutum,* the *primula elatior* and the *primula officinalis*.

Further, there are dry and watery plants that do each other no good. It appears that woody shrubs like lavender cause cucumber, for example, to dry up. On the other hand, cool plants seem to find the proximity of hot plants, such as the horseradish and the Chinese and Spanish radish, very beneficial.

What, after all, does not go on all the time in the plant world, a society in itself? By watching nature, we must discover what plants seek each other out and which avoid each other, so that we do not hinder the plant by making wrong combinations and somewhere disturb the Great Harmony.

5. Friends and Enemies in the Kitchen Garden

The kitchen garden is a matter of continuing concern for its possessor — something that can never be left to itself. However, weeds grow unbidden. This happens because Mother Nature knows which plants it must combine but we make many mistakes through our ignorance. We think we are saving work in weeding and picking by putting down rows and beds of the same crop. But this is not right. Just like humans, plants also like to have their friends around them, which complement them, and not enemies which secrete something that does them harm.

Further, once a crop has been harvested, a different growth must be put on the same ground, taking different substances from the soil and possibly itself putting back what was taken from the soil by its predecessor. Finally, it is good to know that Mother Nature has already begun to prepare the ground. We need not pull up the herbs which she has allowed to grow on it, for this would be an unnecessary duplication of work.

The following are some hints in this connection from experience.

Potatoes

Plant your potatoes with broadbeans between them: this keeps the insects away. Border this plot with French marigolds and you will never have trouble with eelworm, which they frighten off. Horse-radish at each corner of the plot keeps the potatoes healthy.

Particular friends of the potato, giving mutual aid, are the sun-flower, which is not only a fine sight but whose seeds you can eat, dead nettle, sainfoin (a fodder clover), nasturtium, cabbage, sweet corn and peas.

French beans alternating with rows of potato plants seem to keep the Colorado beetle away. These like aubergines even more; planted round the potatoes, therefore, they draw the beetles off and their concentration on the aubergines makes them easy to catch.

Orach grows well close to potatoes but the latter do not then seem to thrive. Orach and goosefoot growing abundantly on the potato plot are one of nature's means of replenishing the soil which the potatoes have in certain respects exhausted.

Strawberries

Strawberries do well if they are well manured and planted alternately with borage. A handful of pine needles scattered between the strawberry plants makes them stronger and tastier; they regain the taste of the wild variety. Lettuce, spinach and dwarf beans also do well between strawberry plants.

Beetroot

This mixes well with dwarf beans, onions and kohlrabi.

Chives

Planted at the foot of the apple tree, these drive away scab.

Beans

Beans do well interspersed with one of the following vegetables: cabbage, cauliflower, carrots, beetroot, cucumber, celery, leeks and cucumber. Sweet corn also thrives between beans: it eats up the nitrogen which the bean produce (like all vetches). Avoid putting climbing beans near to onions, beetroot and kohlrabi.

Stinging Nettles

Do not dig nettles up but eat them each day until midsummer! They enrich the garden soil with calcium, increase the yield from your fruit trees and improve the scent of your aromatic herbs. Planted next to nettles, peppermint produces much more ethereal oils. Stinging nettles round the compost heap cause the waste to break down quicker. On the compost heap, nettles remove the smell. You will also have fine butterflies, since the caterpillar of the comma butterfly feeds on nettle leaves.

Dill

Dill makes your garden smell marvellous. Combine it with maize if you have it but never with carrots. Lettuce, onion and cucumber, too, seem to get along with dill.

Dead Nettle

This plant stimulates all vegetables.

Yarrow

This stimulates all herbs and vegetables.

Marigold

A row of marigolds keeps away the ants and possibly the eelworm.

Rose beds, too, stay healthier with marigold. Tomatoes thrive in their presence and are protected by them against the white tomato fly.

Clover

Clover is good for grass and all vegetables since it binds nitrogen. Buttercups as neighbours will chase it off.

Garlic

Garlic, onions, chives and shallots round fruit trees will keep them healthy. Planted next to roses, they improve their scent. Garlic and onion tea can be sprayed as a means of protecting potatoes and tomatoes against disease. They form nature's best antibiotics.

Cucumber

Cucumbers seem to do well with horse manure. They value sunflowers or maize or potatoes round the bed. Beans, too, and rows of kohlrabi alternating with lettuce or kohlrabi with savoys. If cucumber is to be juicy, it should not be combined with dry and drying plants such as lavender or rosemary.

Cabbage

Plant parsley or hyssop round and amongst cabbage plants to avoid trouble from the cabbage white caterpillars. Beans do well alternating with cabbage (a freshly crushed cabbage leaf laid on any hurt of the body whatever will remove all the ill effects). However, cabbage and marjoram will drive each other into the ground.

Lettuce

Lettuce likes the company of strawberries and small carrots. It softens radishes in its neighbourhood. Drying plants nearby, such as lavender, make it less juicy. (Lettuce contains bromide which induces sleep, so take a few leaves before going to bed.)

Gooseberry

Plant away from blackcurrants.

Fat-hen

Fat-hen (*Chenopodium album*) belongs to the goosefoot family and can be eaten raw or cooked. Where it appears in abundance, no potatoes should be cultivated.

Marjoram

Marjoram drives off spiders, lizards and ants.

Orach

The wild, green orach is stronger and much more tasty than the yellow garden variety. It contains quicksilver. But keep it away from potatoes as it stops them growing.

Horseradish

The sharp horseradish at the corners of the potato plot protects it against all kinds of disease. Horseradish forms large leaves, and needs a lot of space. Two plants may well suffice for kitchen needs. The grated root, only very little of which is required in a milk sauce or in vinegar, can be put back into the ground three times. Take out the root in the autumn or it will spread through the whole garden.

Spraying with horseradish tea, highly diluted (one part in ten), protects apple trees against rust.

Horseradish preserves fruit for five months and eggs for five years.

Mint

Peppermint and spearmint in a tea or sauce keep ants, mosquitoes and other unwanted animals at bay through their strong smell. The proximity of stinging nettles increases their aroma. Camomile planted next to them is improved but takes some of the scent away from the mint. Mint between the vegetables keeps away lice, fleas, the larvae of the blackfly and the caterpillar of the cabbage white. In the home, posies of dried mint can be hung in the clothes cupboard against moths.

Chickweed

The juicy leaves of the chickweed (or stitchwort) are delicious eaten raw, invigorating, cooling, water-reducing and effective against convulsions. This herb spreads horizontally over the ground and so keeps it damp. Weed it as little as possible.

Wallflowers

Wallflower plants are good for apple trees.

Parsley

Parsley is very good for roses and tomatoes.

Radish

Radish stimulates vegetables and is a particularly good influence on peas, nasturtiums and chervil, but not on hyssop.

Rosemary

This keeps away the carrot fly and gets on well with sage.

Scorzonera

Scorzonera helps small carrots against carrot fly.

Comfrey

The cooked root of the comfrey (garden blackwort) has become very popular in Britain as a vegetable. It is a particularly good tonic for the bone structure.

Tomato

Tomatoes and asparagus help each other. Tomatoes benefit from parsley and stinging nettles. However, they should not be planted near to kohlrabi, fennel, potatoes or apricot trees.

The heavy scent of the tomato plant keeps many undesired insects at a distance, particularly the cabbage white caterpillar.

Valerian

Valerian attracts earthworms and cats. It is therefore a good plant for bordering vegetable beds since earthworms keep the ground friable and make it fruitful. An extract can be made from the root with which all plants can be sprayed once a month in order to strengthen their resistance. Valerian tea can be drunk in order to relax and calm the nerves.

Fennel

Fennel damages all other plants in its neighbourhood so sow it in a far corner of the kitchen garden. Fennel itself does badly in the company of coriander and produces no seed if placed close to wormwood or lemon balm.

Violets

The tricolour violet helps rye in the field as well as hare's-foot, sheep's sorrel and cornflower. In turn, rye helps the violet. The flowers can be eaten or they can be made into a syrup for ailments of the mucous membrane of the mouth. In the form of a tea, it can be taken against eczema, together with fumitory and speedwell.

Sunflower

In Russia, sunflowers are always sown round the cornfields, first of all for their seeds, which the harvesters chew the whole day through, and secondly because it keeps the mice away from the grain. Cucumber does well with sunflowers.

The Bee Plants

So that fruiting trees and bushes can be fertilised, it is particularly important to attract bees. If you keep them yourself, plants which are rich in nectar are of course indispensable in the garden. These include: borage, thyme, hyssop, marjoram and oregano, basil, mint, savoury, nepeta, balm, parsley, dill, sunflower, golden rod, elder, privet and dog rose.

The fine buddleia, of course, attracts many butterflies.

Plants Against Undesirable Insects and Other Animals

Carrot fly: Scatter male fern. Spray with a liquid manure of onion, leek or chives.

Caterpillars: Plant sage, hyssop and mint between the vegetables.

Cockchafers: Set garlic between the plants.

Eelworm: Tagetes and marigolds between and round the vegetables; also spray with a marigold manure, i.e. an extract of marigold in rain water which is allowed to stand until the plants form a paste with the water and then use diluted.

Flies: Fresh oak leaves keep flies away, as does the colour blue. Finely-chopped buds of the alder buckthorn will paralyse them.

Leek fly: Scatter pine needles amongst the plants.

Lice and Fleas: Sow nasturtium round the beds, the rambling kind amongst fruit trees. Also spray with a nasturtium manure.

Mice: Leaves of the danewort and the everlasting pea will frighten them off.

Midges: To stop being bitten yourself, rub the fresh leaf of fleabane or mint into the skin. Finely-chopped buds of the alder buckthorn produce a scent that paralyses midges. The fine but poisonous castor-oil plant in the garden keeps midges away. This is the plant that produces the remarkable oil.

Mites: Spray with tobacco water early in the morning while the dew is still on the leaves. Two pounds (900g) of tobacco ribs (waste from a cigarette factory) are boiled in two gallons of water until the latter becomes a deep brown. Dilute this in a one to two ratio with rain water.

Moles: Place a peeled knob of garlic in the ground. Plant spurge round about.

Moths (in clothing or in the carpet): Hang thin bags with dried herbs such as lavender, mint, rosemary or sage together with some wormwood in the clothes cupboard, or lay in the bottom of the cupboard.

Slugs: Scatter sawdust or oak leaves round the vegetable beds.

Strawberry weevil: Scatter fern leaves.

6. Plants as Food

If plants really have feelings, it cannot be very pleasant for them when people pull them up and devour them, after chopping them up and boiling them to death. Vegetarians, who do not want to burden their conscience with the death fear of animals who are driven to the slaughterhouse with premonitions of their fate, are confronted with a similar problem with regard to plants. However, until we learn to live on air alone, we shall have to use plants as food. But a lot depends on how we do this.

When a Balinese is about to kill a chicken in order to eat it, he first says, "Chicken, I have to kill you because I am hungry. Please excuse me!"

That should be our attitude towards plants, too. Perhaps when every community lovingly tends its own garden, the lot of plants will change. They will no longer have the humiliating feeling of being regarded only as a lump of food from birth onwards. In a proper garden, a plant's life will be more natural, with an occasional kind word and a friendly nod — not because they are likely to make a tasty dish, but for their own sakes. And people will then no longer have to commit mass murder on plants, with beds being cleared at a stroke. No. Each day, before each meal, we shall go into the garden and take one or two leaves from each plant which it can easily do without since it continually grows new ones. In this way, we need far fewer plants for food and do far less work accordingly, while the plant is hardly damaged, if at all.

So, if we clean everything, prepare it and eat it raw, with a prayer of thanks that we really mean, a happy relationship may still result between people and plants, even though, unavoidably, it must pass through the painful process of being chewed. But the leaf is only part of its body, not the plant itself. Little by little, we will then perhaps learn to do without the root, stalk, leaf and flower and to suffice with eating only the fruit and seeds.

The plant lets these fall from over-abundance and there are always so many fruits that its procreation need not be threatened if we take a major part of them for our food. Fruit and nuts include grains, nuts, pulses, soft fruits and small seeds — precisely the most nutritious part of a plant, since in its seeds all the plant's energy is compressed. The raw seed contains the enormous life-force which results in a tree or a plant which once again can produce millions of seeds.

The tough Roman soldiers, on foot and crossing mountains and rivers in all kinds of weathers, conquered virtually all of Europe existing each day only on a handful of wheat which they soaked overnight. Should we not, therefore, eventually be able to make do with our muesli of various kinds of germinated corn grains, accompanied, in the cold countries, by fatty, albumen-rich nuts, and in summer by refreshing juicy fruit? For those who do heavy work, add some nourishing pulses, possibly even boiled — but hunger makes raw beans sweet. For the fine palate, sprinkle a little poppy seed, sesame seed, linseed or similar over it, and we can be healthy, strong and satisfied without destroying any plant.

Economic Benefits

If we were to move towards a diet of this kind, to which our teeth are in fact adapted, it would also mean the end of any kind of world food shortage. This is merely the result of our stupidity, short-sightedness and avarice. Wild plants supply vitamins in plenty, and also the major part of the minerals we require. Albumen, carbohydrates and fats are passed on by the mother plant in its seed as reserve food for the germinating plant. The fruit and seeds richest in these have already been cultivated for thousands of years as food crops. The soya bean can provide all the world's peoples with a cheap and outstanding albuminous food. America already grows enough for its whole population, were it to turn vegetarian and so reject animal albumen altogether. But what does it do? It feeds the whole crop to cattle which, when slaughtered, supply in their meat only a small proportion of all the albuminous food that they have consumed throughout their life.

Nor is it necessary to process soya beans in the factory into an 'artificial' meat. As if we could not do without the taste of bacon, ham and steak! In the East, every family has for centuries been making its own cheese-type product from the soya bean — tofu — obtainable from many oriental food stores: the cheapest plant albumen, with an excellent food quality and easily made into a tasty morsel with herbs. It can also be eaten uncooked, like curds, with vegetables or fruit. And as for fats, the healthiest kind of fat is natural oil, pressed from seeds without the application of heat. We have countless oil-bearing seeds at our disposal.

As soon as the pastures now grazed by cattle are ploughed under for cereals, pulses, potatoes and, provisionally, a few vegetables, bordered with fruit trees and nut trees where the birds which will devour the unwanted insects can nest, there will be enough sound and tasty food for everyone. Without poisons, without artificial fertiliser factories, without the death of animal and plant.

Composting with the deposited remains of plants, as Mother Nature does, we shall then have returned to the natural cycle of living things — to the salvation of ourselves and all things.

There is enough soil and water on Earth. And humans have enough intelligence to make the deserts flower, as we have seen in the Negev. Where there is a will, there is a way — if only we have the will.

7. Plants and the Moon

As astrologers know, our present moon (Luna) was originally born from the Earth and still has the closest links with the earthly system. While the sun scatters its seeds of light, which become tangible in the Earth's atmosphere as the immortal cell nuclei of all living beings on Earth, it is the moon which, because it governs the Earth's water, causes the cell to divide and so constructs the embodiments of the sun nuclei. The moon controls the ethereal zone between the Earth, where living and growing things keep each other, and its own course. It governs incarnation and excarnation, the provision of a material shape and its dissolution. In its form as the moon-woman Luna, it accompanies the souls who come to seek a dwelling on Earth in a womb and also the souls of the deceased who have shed their earthly shape. Everything comes from the moon and returns to the moon.

The patterns according to which the moon builds come from the stars and the signs of the zodiac. In this way, the sun, moon and stars are involved in the coming and the going of creatures on Earth.

The moon attracts the water on Earth at that side of the Earth which, at a given point, is turned towards it. In this way, together with the sun, it causes the ebb and flow of the oceans. At the same time, it attracts the water in every living thing. Human, animal and plant are consequently not always equally provided with water.

The moon's effect is the stronger the more of the sun's light it reflects to Earth. Consequently, everything is most endowed with water in the full moon and at its driest in the new moon. In the course of 28 days — the time the moon needs in order to pass once through the zodiac (as seen from the Earth) — two opposite periods can be distinguished:

Waxing moon: The rising of the water and accordingly much cell division, germinating, embodying, incarnation, and concretising of the ethereal patterns into material forms.

Waning moon: Falling of the water and consequently drying and dying, excarnation, and a discarding of material forms.

If we want a plan (i.e. an ethereal pattern in the soul) to run smoothly, its implementation must be begun immediately after the new moon, and its effects will remain for two weeks. (When Hitler, on the advice of his astrologer, began his *blitzkriegs* on the first day after the new moon, a country was conquered in two weeks.) If we make a journey, start building a house or ship, write a book, or start out on a painting, a business deal, marriage or whatever, the best time for a smooth and concrete achievement is immediately after the new moon.

If, however, we want to break something down, demolish, dismantle, dismember or harvest it, we must then begin immediately after the full moon and we have two suitable weeks for doing so.

Effects on Plants

The plant world is connected particularly closely with the moon and its phases, since the moon governs the area of vegetable life. Gardeners will do well to take account of the moon's phases in all their tasks.

Sowing is done during the waxing moon; rapidly germinating seed a few days after the new moon; slowly germinating seed earlier.

Planting, where strong roots have to be formed, must be done in the evening or at night in a waning moon, because the water then runs to the roots.

Harvesting of vegetables or fruit which are to be as juicy as possible is done immediately after the full moon.

Chopping of wood which is to serve as timber or firewood, and must therefore be as dry as possible, is done in a waning moon, shortly before the new moon.

Pruning of a hedge (or cutting the hair of the head) is done, if we want the hedge (or hair) to be thicker, at the start of the waxing moon; but if we want less growth, in a waning moon. Cabbage gathered for pickling and cut in a waxing moon close to the full moon will cause the barrel to overflow!

Inoculations and vaccinations are of course done in a waxing moon.

With a root (carrot or beetroot) we can tell by the rings how many months old the root was when it was harvested, since every waxing moon adds a ring in the same way as a tree makes year-rings. An onion acquires a skin with every waxing moon. There are true moon-plants which produce a new leaf daily in a waxing moon and drop a leaf daily in a waning moon.

Critical Days and Signs

The days on which the new moon, first quarter, full moon and last quarter precisely fall are critical and useless for anything, i.e. from three hours before the precise time to three hours after it. These times can be found in many newspapers and calendars, in almanacs and also in astrologers' ephemerides. Important for work in the garden is choosing the sign of the zodiac through which the moon is passing. It is common sense that water signs are suitable for wet working, earth signs for work on the soil, such as sowing, transplanting, setting-out, digging. Air signs are suitable only for sowing and staking plants that grow rapidly, such as those that climb (trailing beans, vetches). Fire signs are suitable only for harvesting hot crops (radish, garden cress, horseradish, mustard, black radish, nasturtium seed) because they are then at their hottest. Further, always sow during earth or water signs. They are the fruitful signs, particularly Taurus, Cancer, Scorpio and Pisces. Never harvest anything in Pisces, as it decays rapidly.

Manuring is best done in Scorpio, in the last quarter, and weeding in Virgo. Potatoes and bulbs should be planted in a waning moon, in an earth sign, unless they are to come up quickly. Flowers should be sown in Aries, Libra or Virgo. Sow and harvest vegetables for preserving in Aries (long-lasting seed).

Anything that is to produce a tender leaf and mellow fruit should preferably be sown in water signs: Cancer, Scorpio or Pisces (but in Pisces only if it is to be eaten immediately). What is to grow underground (corms, bulbs and roots) needs an earth sign: Taurus, Virgo or Aries. Flowers and climbing plants are sown in air signs: ramblers in Gemini (strawberries, climbing beans, trailing nasturtium), and flowers in Libra, which is also the sign best for planting fruit trees in a waning moon. Aquarius is unfavourable.

Fire signs are generally unfavourable, being too hot, but plants may be sown in Aries for rapid growth and in Sagittarius for rapid gain in height. Seed is best obtained in the last week of a waning moon and fruit for preserving harvested in the last quarter, in Taurus. Cereals are harvested in a waxing moon, in Aries, Leo or Aquarius, when the sign indicates dryness but the grains are still large. Spray medically, for example with a stinging nettle manure, in Virgo or Scorpio.

Moon Plants

There are, of course, true moon plants. These are, in the first place, those that open or smell the strongest during the evening or at night and then attract the night moths for pollination, such as the honeysuckle. Especially remarkable is the evening primrose, which is to be found both cultivated in gardens and in the wild. In the gloaming, when the moon rises, it begins to turn its head and then suddenly, unwrapped, springs open.

Honesty, too, is a moon plant. Why would it otherwise be called *Lunaria*? Beans and the plants that belong to the *solanaceae* family, such as the nightshade, bittersweet, potato, tobacco and tomato, and the night-flowering cactus, called the Queen of the Night (*Selenicereus grandiflorus*), are all moon plants.

All water-rich plants are true children of the moon, such as the cucumber, pumpkin, melon and those living in and on the water, such as the water-lily and brandy-bottle, and on the bank, such as the willow. Also the plants with half-moon-shaped leaves or oval leaves — composed of two half-moons.

Like a person, a plant never, of course, belongs to one heavenly body or sign alone; they are named after the sign or star which clearly predominates in form and habits. In humans, moon plants promote the creation and flow of fluids, such as the operation of glands, menstruation, the excretion of urine and sweating. That is why cucumber juice is good for promoting better circulation during a woman's menopause.

Climbing moon-plants twist to the left (*yin*) and can be recognised by that (e.g. *Thunbergia alata*). Those that turn to the right are of the sun (e.g. hops).

In humans, moon plants can be used for ailments (e.g. chickweed against convulsions), for the memory (cashew nuts, as curved as the horned-moon) and for children at school. Climbing *papilionaceae* can be a great tonic to the nervous system and, as a food crop, extremely nutritious (beans). Vetches can be used against infantile paralysis and *Nux vomica* to strengthen the nerves.

8. Plants and Radiation

Plants certainly react just as strongly as humans to vibrations and radiation. But we take so little notice of our own reactions. It is the plants who reveal to us what we ourselves have more than half forgotten.

Plants correspond with the life body of humans — our force field, criss-crossed with electrical and magnetic currents. They manifest these currents through their appearance and condition. Animals instinctively avoid places where the electromagnetic condition is unfavourable. It is only we, whose rational mind blots out the warnings of the instinct, who become aware of harmful radiation when it is too late — through its consequences. Before we learn to believe in our instinct, we can read from the plants what we do not allow to penetrate our conscious mind.

Earth Radiation

What we call 'earth rays' result from cosmic rays encountering certain substances or situations in the soil. Well known are the crossings of underground water courses which disturb the harmony in the life body of plant, animal and human. Farmers know that their cattle will not sleep at certain points in the cowshed but pull the straw away to a better spot. If a water diviner then looks into the matter, the place rejected by a cow or pig will be found to display earth radiation.

However, certain plants prefer to grow on earth radiation and to absorb its vibrations — these include strawberries, shepherd's purse, deadly nightshade and, in particular, stinging nettles and mistletoe.

If your bed stands above earth radiation and it cannot be moved to a better place, you can protect yourself by continually placing fresh nettles or ferns beneath the bed or, better still, sleeping on a mattress filled with dried ferns and nettles. In the past, a child's mattress was always stuffed with ferns or seagrass, particularly the male fern (*Aspidium filix-mas*). These also protect the sleeper against rickets, rheumatism, cramp and pain in the legs (i.e. they are anti-saturnine).

The strawberry converts the radiation to radioactivity in the seeds, which sit on the fleshy base of the fruit. It is because of this radioactivity that some people react to strawberries.

Mistletoe

The case of the mistletoe is a remarkable one. The mistletoe was highly prized in the Celtic culture of our ancestors. On the sixth day after the new moon, the Druids went, wrapped in long white linen cloaks, and cut the mistletoe from the oak tree with a silver sickle. It was placed on linen and later processed into an amulet or medicine, especially against epilepsy and 'king's evil'. Later, like so many holy medicinal herbs of antiquity, it was declared a devil's growth and the authorities ordered farmers and fruit-growers to root out the mistletoe wherever it appeared on oaks and fruit trees. Through short-sighted self-interest, this plant, which does not make ordinary roots but only suckers which suck the sap from the branches of trees, was regarded as a harmful parasite — until, in modern times, someone discovered that the mistletoe only occurs on trees which are already slightly diseased, i.e. are cancerous. The longer the mistletoe 'feeds off' these trees, the more the cancerous swellings disappear!

Trees with cancer will be found at places with earth radiation, as will people and animals who suffer from this disease. What does the mistletoe in fact do? It absorbs both the radiation and the poison that the radiation has caused within the organism which was unable to cope with it.

Force Fields

Earth radiation gives rise to a force field turning to the right, which leads to condensation, creation in matter, incarnation. Too much of this leads to the creation of superfluous forms — swellings. This is not an absolute excess but a relative one, through a resistance set up by the expansion of a limit. The mistletoe and the left-turning climbing plants (e.g. bind weed) have a left-turning force field (life body). These are moon plants. The right-turning life bodies will be found amongst the sun plants. The African wind-flower is very sensitive to earth radiation. Where it flourishes, there is no radiation.

Earth radiation is not harmful to all people, animals and plants. Those who are physically weak (*yin*) and over-sensitive could best do with some earth radiation (*yang*). In the animal world, there are those who thrive on earth radiation — ants, bees, cats and owls. Ant hills are built above earth radiation and ant tracks pass along underground water courses. To keep ants away, plant marigolds around the house; they are also a curative against cancer.

Swarms of bees will seek out a radiated place for settling and the greater the radiation the greater and more industrious the swarm. Wild bees like to build their nests in a hollow tree which is ailing and, lo and behold, the tree recovers. Through the formic acid in the honey, added by the bee to the nectar it gathers, the air is insulated against the radiation. Bee's poison ('apis' in homoeopathy) is a specific against ailments aggravated by earth radiation — rheumatism and cancer. Beekeepers seldom suffer from these diseases. Midges, too, like to dance above a radiated spot.

Animals that avoid earth radiation are, amongst others, dogs, storks and pigs. (Dogs are *yang*, extrovert, while cats are *yin* and introvert.) Where the stork builds its nest there is no earth radiation.

Since lightning tends to strike above water courses, it is a common superstition that the stork protects against lightning. Plants which protect against this, such as the house leek, also act as medicaments against cancer and the like.

Aquarium plants flourish on earth radiation, i.e. above water courses. Water is analogous with the moon and with the affective life of human and animal. Thus, in ourselves, we can see that our sensitivity and nervous irritability become greater the more our body contains water.

9. The Plant as a Dowsing Rod

Dowsing is research at an ethereal level. The vibrations of the stars can be dowsed as can those of the soil, whose hidden treasures, waters and ores send their vibrations to the surface. As of old, the instrument used for this purpose is the dowsing rod, a forked hazel twig, grown in the spring and cut in midsummer on the correct day and at the precise planet-time. This can be used for finding earth radiation and ores. However, to indicate water a forked willow twig must be used, because willow is closely linked with water.

The hazel tree is approached backwards with a new knife christened in holy water, preferably in the night preceding the longest light (21 June) towards midnight. The selected twig is pulled forwards between the legs with the left hand, which is wrapped in white linen, a suitable exorcism is spoken, and the twig is cut off. The rod is always used by the same person and by no one else, solemnly and silently. A sign is placed at the two ends forming the fork to know which should be held by the left and which by the right hand, since the rod becomes used to its owner and adapts the course of its molecules in such a way that the personal current of the dowser passes through as smoothly as possible.

The hazelnut is an ancient holy tree, very favourably inclined to humans. Eating hazelnuts increases the blood pressure and dilates the blood vessels. In antiquity, the homes of wise women were often surrounded with hazelnut trees.

If the dowser holds the two ends of the rod in his hands and walks forward, the third end will, at a certain point, deflect forcefully downwards — this is where what is sought is located. The number of times it bobs down, so many metres does it lie beneath the surface (at least if the dowser has arranged this with his rod). He must adapt the rod beforehand with his force of mind to what he is seeking, whether this be earth radiation or water or buried treasure or the foundations of earlier buildings, or whatever. The vibrations of the dowser's mind and those of what he seeks meet through the rod.

Plant Indicators

To find certain substances and ores in the soil, no dowsing rod is in fact necessary. The location alone of many plants indicates that the ground contains the substances that the plant needs for its development and special properties.

In Britain, a plant is found growing wild which is really more at home in warmer climes, in Mexico and Asia — the sumac (*Rhus toxicodendron*), which is used homoeopathically as a medicine against rheumatism. It calms the nerves and is also a toxic narcotic. We detect a feeling of unease even in the neighbourhood of the plant and gardeners who have sawn branches from it have been blinded by it. In the evening, when it emits a strong smell, it can cause a rash. The sap is used for plumbing and paints. Where this plant grows, the soil contains lead ore. This belongs to Saturn, as does rheumatism.

In China, Japan and Queensland we find the ornamental cherry, which betrays the presence of gold and silver ore.

In America, the mirabilis flower indicates silver, as does the palm lily (*Yucca filamentosa*) in Mexico and a kind of knot-grass in Montana.

Meadow rue and hemp agrimony indicate copper and in France new coal deposits have been discovered by the presence of the *Lepidodendron*.

In South Africa, the water thorn indicates diamond fields.

Lead is indicated by the butterbur in the Sieg area of West Germany. If we want to know where platinum ore is deposited, we must find areas where no plant grows at all.

In Spain, people know that phosphates are found where a certain type of bind weed grows.

Each plant germinates where it finds the nourishment suited to it. We therefore know that on acid ground Mother Nature causes the major de-acidifiers and lime-providers to thrive, such as the daisy, dock and wood sorrel, and that rhododendrons and azaleas grow particularly well on it. Beeches and the blackthorn prosper on chalk. The bramble is at its tastiest on loam and loess, and where sand and loam border on each other we find the field thistle.

On silt beaches we find the salt-lovers or halogens, such as scurry-grass, salsola, sea blight, sea orach and sea lavender. The water is good for drinking where watercress grows.

Poisonous gas can be discovered by tomato plants which roll up their leaves if, for example, the natural gas content in the air reaches 1 in 200,000.

Plants of the *Astragalus* family attract the semi-metal selenium from the earth's crust, which belongs to the moon. This is distributed very finely through the earth and is therefore difficult and expensive to obtain. The ash of these plants is sometimes found to contain a thousand times as much selenium as the earth on which the plant grows. As a result, the occupation of selenium farming has appeared in the USA, where *Astragalus* is planted (for example, in Nebraska). The selenium harvest can amount to more than a hundredweight per hectare. The *Astragalus* is a *Papilionaceae*, one variety of which, the liquorice vetch, *Astragalus molissimus*, which is found in Europe, Asia and Canada, contains the same substance (glycyrrhizine) as common liquorice and this property is referred to in its name in various languages — 'drop-plant' in Dutch, 'reglisse sauvage' in French, and 'lackritz-wicke' in German. Its effect on humans is refreshing and tonic; it is a hydrofuge and expectorant.

A different kind is the tragacanth, a bush which grows in Asia Minor, Southern Russia and the Himalayas. Its effect is adhesive, emollient and laxative.

Liquorice vetch is apparently the kind that attracts selenium.

10. The Plant as Alchemist

It takes some time for the old truths from the first phase of the development of the human mind to be rediscovered in the third. In between lies the second or rational phase, in which simplified thinking seeks the aid of only material phenomena and constructs a link between these and a lower level of understanding. It was, therefore, long thought that only a certain number of substances existed whose atoms did not change. That is a reassuring idea. Science is in fact rather too much under the influence of Saturn, the force of formulation but also of solidification, which causes everything to be conceived of statically. Although there already were scholars in the 18th century who discovered that substances appeared to be created from nothing, investigation did not as yet go much further.

A small boy in Brittany, whose father kept hens in a run, wondered where the hens found the calcium for the eggs they laid each day. After all, they never were given shells or other forms of calcium to peck. But when it had rained and afterwards the sun reappeared, shining particles of mica could be seen on the granite-bearing ground, which the chickens avidly pecked up. When his mother killed one of the hens, neither mica nor chalk was to be found in its stomach. Where did the mica go to and where did the calcium come from? Tests showed that a hen produces five times as much calcium in its eggshell and manure as appears in its feed!

The boy was called Louis Kervran, who later, as a chemist, pondered the problems which he had become aware of from childhood onwards and then, in the 1950s, after extensive experiments, came to the conclusion that living beings are able to convert one substance to another, in the way that the hen converts mica to the calcium that it needs for its eggshells. Humans and animals carry a great alchemist with them — their liver. This converts whatever is available into what the body needs for its work.

Internal Alchemy

The simplified thinking of the second phase tends to regard the human body as a tube full of chemical substances. If blood analysis shows that one or other substance is deficient, the substance is quite simply topped up, for example iron pills for iron deficiency. It now appeared, however, that in many cases it was better to apply a different substance from which the body itself makes whatever is lacking. If there is a shortage of iron, it is better to take manganese and/or magnesium, not in the pure form but through natural vegetable food.

For example, manganese appears in large quantities in almonds and magnesium in camomile. If an organism needs calcium, then it is best to take organic silicic acid and silicates, for example in the herb horsetail. How often does it not happen that people with a Saturn affliction are deficient in calcium, despite the many calcium preparations they take. The calcium is just not absorbed by the blood. It has now been found that the human body cannot absorb the calcium from food if there is too little magnesium present. Too little phosphorus may also then be ingested, however much albuminous food we eat.

This is very interesting from the medical-astrological perspective. If in a double affliction, Saturn (calcium) is stronger than the sun (magnesium), what results is not a surplus of calcium (which should happen according to the simplified thinking of Bartjes) but a calcium deficiency, because in fact the intake or production of magnesium is inhibited. A living organism cannot be understood merely by adding and subtracting. Why is manganese good against allergies? Because it stimulates the creation of iron which belongs to Mars (defensive strength).

When seeds germinate, it has been observed that iron results and manganese disappears. The conversion of the one substance into the other is due to an enzyme. The reverse also occurs: Kervran discovered the bacteria which convert iron to manganese. This discovery is already used industrially in Japan. Bacteria of this kind live in the healthy human intestine.

Not all plants can bring all changes about. Rye, for example, can make its own manganese to requirement, but wheat cannot. In agriculture, it is not sufficient to take the view that the substances which in the main are obtained from the soil by the harvested crops should just be returned in the form of artificial fertiliser. Such all too simple thinking overlooks the processes of the living plant itself. These are largely helped by micro-organisms living in the roots of the plant. The enzymes — the true alchemists in plant, animal and human — must be fed with 'oligo-elements', which can be done by making extracts of certain plants and spraying it on the soil and young growth. This can be made from stinging nettles and horsetail.

Plant Chemistry

When a field appears to be smothered by a certain kind of so-called weed, it is worth leaving the field fallow for a year. The wild plant returns the substances to the soil which it lacks. Even the biblical laws of Moses prescribe that a field should be left fallow for one year in seven to let it recover. And Charlemagne laid down the three-year system: every field must be left fallow one year in three. Land is therefore divided into three parts, and each year two of them are tilled. If there is an urgent need for all the land to be tilled, the weed appearing is removed and placed on the compost heap. Once it has changed to earth, it is spread out on the same field where it has grown and it will saturate the soil just as effectively; the next year the weed will have disappeared without trace.

Azaleas grow on acid soil, such as heathland, where no chalk occurs. However, they make so much chalk themselves that sometimes, after a few years, if they are to be retained, a layer of soil, which is then very rich in chalk, must be removed and replaced with acid soil. Plants of this kind like a soil rich in silicates, which they convert to chalk. The conversion to chalk is also influenced by the moon phase in which germination commences.

There are also plants which make their chalk from potassium in the ground. Yeast and microscopic seaweeds make potassium from sodium. Others make it from chalk. If too much potassium is supplied in the form of artificial fertiliser, tomatoes, for example, will become deficient in chalk. Too much potassium, even in the form of a natural manure, also leads to a shortage of molybdenum. Too little potassium produces too much molybdenum. It is all a question of balance.

Plants make potassium in different ways — from sodium, with the aid of oxygen in the air, or from chalk, from which hydrogen is extracted. It once happened that a field was sown with clover for 17 years running. It was mown three times a year. Fertiliser was never scattered. Nonetheless, the harvest of all those years together contained 2636 kg of calcium, 1255 kg of magnesium, 2150 kg of potassium, 1255 kg of phosphoric acid and 2636 kg of nitrogen.

It is not, of course, all that simple. We cannot just say that if only one element is present, the plant will make from it all the others that it needs. In fact, various conditions must be met before transmutation can occur. One of these is that a small quantity of the required new element must already be present. This reminds us of the accounts of alchemical processes, in which a small quantity of gold always had to be present at the start if ultimately new gold was to be made from another element. This small quantity acts as a stimulus. Perhaps, too, this is why the alchemists needed certain plants, which contained this small quantity.

In most transmutations, micro-organisms must also cooperate. In humans and animals, certain glands cooperate in the process with internal secretions. Thus, the thyroid gland produces the enzyme we require to make calcium from other substances if the body contains too little.

Calcium deficiency is not cured by adding calcium, but by adding magnesium and silicates, for example for broken nails. The surplus of potassium in vegetables grown with artificial fertiliser can bring about sudden stopping of the heart and many other modern illnesses through calcium deficiency. Too much potassium in many cases blocks the magnesium from which the body must manufacture the calcium.

A non-salt diet can be very dangerous since chloride deficiency can then occur and the body needs chloride not only for its own functioning but also because it must make another element from it.

After the last war, certain plants appeared in abundance on spoil heaps, even where atomic bombs had been dropped. These plants transmute the radioactive waste into other substances. Nature is so wonderfully dedicated to maintaining life. The stupid errors in human thinking and conduct have already been accounted for. Anyone who learns from nature must forget everything taught at school and he or she will then find a solution to their problems.

11. Herbs of the Alchemists

It has long been known that when making gold by alchemy the aid of a plant has to be called on at a certain stage. But which one? That was always kept very secret. The Atlanteans were well versed in this art of transmutation. Atlanteans who survived the demise of their country in the Atlantic ocean still live and work, both within the earth's crust and in caves and hollowed-out mountains. A doctor from Los Angeles, Dr Doreal, a theosophist, once attended a lecture on an occult subject and afterwards found two men in wait for him, who asked him whether he would himself like to see what had been discussed. With his permission, they drove into the desert with him, where they got out. He was given a belt with a few knobs on it, and a kind of helmet. They then stood either side of him and held him firmly under the arms. Together with them, he then had to press one of the buttons and all three rose upwards at great speed, rushed through the air and landed a little later on a mountain slope. This later proved to be Mount Shasta, in the extreme north of California. They had landed on a platform which moved downwards like a lift and here they entered a large building inside the mountain, full of passages and rooms.

The visitor was shown a great many things, including how gold was made from sand. A metallic drawer was pulled from a tall cabinet, sand was strewn on it and it was returned to the cabinet. A little later, it was pulled out again, covered in gold in place of the sand. With lumps of this gold these people pay for the few things, such as sea salt, which they buy from the small shops in the surrounding countryside. However, Dr Doreal never learned the secret.

Parallel Processes

In medieval Europe, now and again someone was reincarnated who was able to remember something of it and had only to recall all the details. Such persons understood the secret language of tradition, which remained hidden to others. Alchemy is the artificial acceleration of a natural process, running parallel to the artificial acceleration of the human soul process by exercises in soul functions, in consecutive stages, each of which is introduced with a dedication. In this way, substances, like souls, are enriched, refined, and raised to a higher vibration. Making gold (of the sun) from lead (of Saturn) is the counterpart of the path that runs from the soul ego to the spirit ego.

On these paths, aids to acceleration are available in nature. The toxin of a toadstool (for example, psilocybin) can be used to achieve the experience of cosmic unity, and high homoeopathic potencies of all kinds of plants can help the human soul forwards with a single leap, for example totally curing drunkards or sex maniacs.

The same happens when gold is made from other metals. The sap of a particular plant can, through its creative strength, change the molecular structure of a metal. Such plants may belong to the family of *Rosaceae* — the plant family associated with the sun and the sign Leo — which belongs to gold by its vibration, as in the case, for example, of lady's mantle (alchemilla).

The herbs may also be of the type containing radium, because radium accelerates change. Use can then be made of, for example, the fern-root (filix) which is so highly radioactive that it can contain 52 mache units, which has been proved in a chemical laboratory, while the strongest radioactive source in Switzerland, the Iberger Berggeist in the canton of Schwyz, contains only 2.22 mache units. The well known leader of the theosophists Dr Franz Hartmann (1838-1912), who also wrote a book about Paracelsus and developed the so-called lignosulphite healing method, has also watched the root stock of the male fern glow on St John's eve, the night before the longest day. After all, that night is a very special one, in which the sun's force in many plants reaches its zenith, as for example in the St John's wort (Hypericum), which would also seem to be very useful for alchemists. Other radioactive plants are parsley, leopard's bane, rosemary, and the fruit of the horse-chestnut.

Legends of Gold-Makers

There are many stories about gold-makers who go off to seek a certain plant. Before sunrise on certain days, the alchemists used to go with glass plates to the lady's mantle, whose round leaf, folded like an umbrella, retains a drop of morning dew. This was caught on the glass and was used in the alchemical process. The chevalier Casimir of Khledovski (1843—1920) tells of an Italian who secretly picked a certain plant in the park of a prince. Caught by a servant, he was taken before the prince and was able to purchase his freedom by using the plant to create molten gold. The plant was reduced to ashes and thrown on the melting metal. The prince may well have been Count Palambara, a friend of Queen Christina of Sweden, to whose palace a young man once came asking whether he could conduct alchemical tests in the palace. She agreed and he, after spending several months on his mysterious work, informed the Queen that he had to go and look for a certain plant and asked whether his equipment could be kept in a locked room while he did so. The latter included two crucibles containing a liquid which could be changed to gold with the aid of that plant. And that is what happened. However, he never returned and the Queen had the rooms opened. Here they found two earthen crucibles, the one filled with silver and the other with gold of prime quality.

Count Maximilian of Palambara laughed at Queen Christina when she told him this. Shortly afterwards, a pilgrim appeared at the Count's palace, asking him whether he could pick a plant in his garden which could change everything into gold. The Count made his own laboratory available to him. The pilgrim roasted the herb, rubbed it down into a powder and shook this into an earthen crucible, in which a viscous fluid was boiling. He then asked whether he could use the adjoining room to spend the night in, so that he could keep watch on what was happening. The gold would be ready the next morning. However, when the Count entered his laboratory that morning, the pilgrim had disappeared. The crucible had fallen over and a fluid had flowed from it which had solidified into pure gold. On the table lay papers with passages in Hebrew and Latin which no one could translate. The Count then had the text engraved over a marble gateway which still stands in the park in the Piazza Victor Emanuele in Rome. This is not revealed by the source — the book *Nuova Mescellanea Archeologica* by the Countess Ersilia Caetani-Lovatelli, which appeared in 1874. She calls it the magic gateway of Esquilin. But whether the plant was alchemilla or another, we do not know.

Another herb of the alchemists is the moon wort (*Botrychium lunaria*), with its half-moon-shaped leaf, which can be used quite simply to help make silver, gold and even the touchstone. It is also called witch's wort and walburga's wort. It should be used on St Ann's eve, i.e. the night before 1 May, when all elemental spirits are particularly active. The moon wort belongs to the *Ophiaglossaceae* and is found throughout Europe. Herbalists regarded it as a healing herb for wounds.

Transmutation

The gold-maker Tausend, born in 1883, wrote a booklet in 1922 entitled *180 Elements, Their Atomic Weights and Their Place in the Harmonic-Periodic System*. His theory is that the same ratio exists between chemical elements as between the tones in music. Each tone and each element has its own vibration count. In the same way that we can modulate from the one key to another, so can the one element be modulated into another (transmutation) if only we know the vibration counts. Tausend is said to have revealed how he made iron oxide compounds and lead alloys from quartz which on being melted down produced gold. For example, 30 grams of iron oxide produced 0.3 grams of gold.

It appears that Tausend possessed a substance with irradiating effects (radium?) which drew the forces from materials like a magnet. Tausend said that elements obtained from organic substances were the best suited for transmutation and that the ash of plants contained clear identifying signs for transmutation in its salts, lying within the circuit of the atoms. Although his knowledge and art were proven up to and including his 'Small Work', in which 10 grams of gold were obtained, Tausend was put in prison, so that his work came to an end. He was released in February 1933. While in prison, he confided in the rune specialist Marby that gold-in-being is present everywhere in nature, particularly in quartz rock and in the plant kingdom in the flowers of the sun, such as the sunflower. If the pith from the stalk of the sunflower is allowed to dry above a light flame, it acquires a golden sheen. According to Claude Louis, Count of Bertholet, who obtained 40.32 grams of gold from 5 hundredweight of vegetable ash, the ash of all plants contains gold. Rye, too, contains a trace of gold.

To create silver the alchemist needs not only flowers of the sun but also of the moon. In addition to moon wort, referred to above, the moon's area of activities includes chiefly the algae, which are often radioactive — for example quaking algae, a jellylike growth, as transparent as a jellyfish, and wrinkled, black and opaque in dried form, which suddenly appears on sandy paths and in gardens after warm rain and in certain phases of the moon. Someone who was camping in a wood in the Veluwe in Holland once wrote to me saying that one morning he had suddenly found the forest floor covered with this slippery substance. In the past, it was used as a curative for stubborn ulcerations. A short while ago, a report appeared in American newspapers on a growth of this kind that suddenly appeared in city gardens in the form of red bubbles, which quickly multiplied and pulsed. They were ineradicable and appeared in more and more places. Botanists did not know what to do with them. We feel, however, that they are algae, originating under the influence of the moon and sometimes referred to in legend as 'moon food'.

Ordinary fresh water algae, particularly the type Zygnema,

contain a hundred times as much radium as sea algae, which fluoresce. They are richer in radium than the richest granite ores containing it. Through cumulation, the algae assemble their riches in a radium-free environment.

12. Plants Against Fire

Now and again, we read about people of the West Indies or of the South Sea Islands who are able to walk on hot coals without burning themselves. This is often a component of some religious ceremony. Western observers assume that it is a question of a concentration of thought. The material body is then so strongly irradiated with spiritual force that it is carried, as it were, beyond the laws of material nature. Even holding on to such a person can make one temporarily fireproof.

It is easier to call on the strength of plants. In the Middle Ages, people who were accused of witchcraft had to prove their innocence by emerging unharmed from a fire test of that kind. People were no doubt thinking of the three young men in the fiery furnace in the book of Daniel, who were not touched by the fire but were protected by an angel.

Ancient Recipes against Fire

A few recipes have come down to us from those ancient times for preparing an ointment from plants which had to be rubbed into the parts of the body to undergo the test, to prevent the fire from gaining any hold on it. One fakir recipe runs as follows. If the hands are rubbed with the juice of a poplar or of herb mercury, then boiling hot molten lead can be poured on the hands without it doing any harm. A French recipe: an ointment is prepared from the juice of marshmallow (*Altheae*), parsley seed and chalk, ground fine and mixed with egg white and the juice of a horseradish. As soon as this has dried, a second layer is rubbed over the top. When this, too, has dried, glowing iron can be carried in the hands without burning. If the whole body has been rubbed in this way, you can walk through fire.

A similar recipe uses marshmallow juice, fresh egg white, the seed of the plantain (*Plantago psyllium*), finely ground chalk and the juice of horseradish. Yet another recipe states: red arsenic and alum are powdered and mixed with the juice of the house leek and laurel resin. Anointed with this ointment, the person becomes fireproof. Sometimes, ox gall is added.

Other herbs mentioned for the same purpose are celandine (*Chelidonium*), crocus, Indian aloe and danewort.

The yogi Swami Narayananda Saraswati (born in 1922) had the following experience. He had studied medicine in the USA and was a surgeon at a Madras hospital until 1947. In 1952, he met a lama in the Himalayan village of Sava in Bhutan, who stood in a cave in the centre of a flaming fire, naked and covered with an ointment. Not a hair was even scorched. The ointment consisted of four herbs which the yogi had learned to mix, after painful tests, in a certain composition. When he himself had rubbed his hands with the same salve at his home in Hardwar and was repairing an electrical appliance, he accidentally touched the live wire, but without any ill-effects. He then had his body partly rubbed with the ointment and exposed to X-rays. The parts anointed were not penetrated by the rays. He is now conducting research with scientists into whether the mixture could also act as protection against radioactivity.

The herbs aloe and house leek and the seed of the flea-bane have a strong cooling effect. Conversely, horseradish and celandine are sharp and hot. It is not simple to explain the effect of these herbs in this case. Apparently, the concentration of thought and the ointment combine to produce the desired effect.

13. Plant Elves

That many people are unable to see plant elves does not mean that they do not exist. From time immemorial, many people have observed them and even conversed with them. The ancient Greeks called them dryads, the Germans *waldweiblein* or *moosweiblein*, and the Dutch *planten-elfen*, and while we speak generally of fairies, we also distinguish between various kinds. In Ireland, they are still part of local life.

In Scotland, in Morayshire, there is the Findhorn Community where beautiful gardens were constructed in cooperation with the plant elves who have been seen by some of the clairvoyant workers. Once, a flowering whin that leaned right across the path had been pruned. At the daily meeting, the clairvoyants reported that the elves were all fleeing in horror. It was decided to consult them. Eventually, humans and elves agreed that, if really necessary, bushes could be pruned from time to time, but then only before they were in flower.

That, of course, is something that sensitive people do of their own accord. We thank a plant for the enjoyment its flowering gives us. Ingratitude hurts the plant elf. It is wrong for people who have been given a house plant simply to throw it away when it has finished blooming, as if a plant is not also a fine and beneficial thing without blooms, and does not want to go on living!

A plant elf is an ethereal being who has been given the task to look after and protect the plant. It attracts insects for pollination, and closes the flower or bends it over when it rains. It has a human shape and dresses in a colour that fits the plant. The well-loved books by the illustrator Cicely Mary Barker portray the elves, accompanied with simple children's verses. A book containing many accounts of elves and other creatures of nature is *The Kingdom of Faerie* by Geoffrey Hodson, who writes from his own observation. Another book by this author is *Fairies at Work and at Play*[1].

A German book on this subject is one by Karl Spiesberger, *Elementargeister, Naturgeister*[2].

That elves, fairies and other small folk are more commonly seen in Britain and Ireland than in the Netherlands is due to the very damp atmosphere of these islands, through which ethereal forms are more easily observed by humans. They are not visible in bright sunlight, but can be seen in fog, mist and drizzle, and also at twilight or in moonlight.

The plant elf hovers in the air and now and then spreads itself over the plant, so as to impart its life force to it. It will then briefly waft away in order to recharge itself with new sun energy. They

[1] published by the Theosophical Publishing House Ltd, London
[2] published by Bauer Verlag, Freiburg

will fly to a height of about three metres, some having wings like butterflies, others showing only a small face but otherwise a flowing shape or aura, always permeated with moving waves of soft colours. An elf is more highly charged than a human and experiences contact with a human force field as a heavy weight. They see our ethereal bodies and not our physical ones, and therefore know exactly what our intentions are — an elf cannot be deceived.

The Nature of Elves

There are elves no taller than the grass stalks amongst which they live and others whose size will vary between that of a child and that of a fully grown human.

In the summer, they like to live in the flowering meadows, where they receive instruction from their leaders, who in turn obey the king of the elves, a splendid being who radiates light and lustre. In inclement weather and during the winter, the elves withdraw into hollow trees, or into the earth — since, as they are ethereal, they can pass through any solid substance.

Elves are sexless and do not procreate themselves. They gradually develop from more simple beings. The whole kingdom of natural creatures begins with sunbeams, or light seeds, which the sun continuously broadcasts into the solar system. When they penetrate the Earth's atmosphere, they first take shape in the small icicles that form fluffy clouds. Here they are given their first task. They then come to Earth in the form of raindrops, hailstones and snowflakes. Once they have arrived at the Earth's crust, they attach themselves in friendship to a plant and through mutual cooperation develop into a plant elf.

The plant elf is, as it were, the external soul of the plant and acts as its guardian. It supplies what it needs, as far as possible, and the plant accepts it. This is quite different from us humans, who by no means always accept what our angels supply for our salvation. Plant and elf obey the cosmic laws and the precepts of their leaders; they cannot be disobedient.

Plants possess an earthly body and a material form. Amongst the more highly developed plants, there are the beginnings of a sensitive soul or astral body, which their elf also acquires. An example is the columbine, which has reached the end of a long, centuries-old period of development and with its refined pattern belongs to the ancient nobility of the plant world. It also has a refined elf to serve it.

In the case of annuals, when the plant dies in the autumn, its elf is of course dismissed from its service. After a winter of instruction in the earth, it then again appears in the spring and takes a newly germinated plant under its protection. With perennials, the elf always stays with the same plant.

Official science, which limits itself to the material, says that the plant turns its flower towards the sun, closes when it rains, produces red dye for heat in cold weather, and avoids plants which secrete substances which are harmful to it as a result of a built-in pattern of chemical reactions, and not through the aid of the elf. The chemical and other reactions of course exist, but they form the material aspect of the entire life process. At the ethereal level, it is the elf that causes this built-in pattern to work. There is only one process in operation, completed at each stage of materialisation in the apparent forms appropriate to that stage.

Elves copy humans in many ways, but conversely people have adopted many of the elves' ways. From where do we get our word 'ball' for a dancing party? When elves dance in the moonlight, circulating with arms raised, they create eddies in the ether, a ball consisting of the life force (*prana*). This force they later pass on to their plants. It is the same vortex of forces created by ritual at an altar.

Each dance leaves invisible but highly effective tracks in the ether: magnetic lines. What its effect will be will depend on the series of movements. When people dance, for instance if they waltz, swirls of energy are created, for which the tension between the sexes acts as a power source. The intention is that this will produce a state of bliss, a fullness of happiness in the consciousness of the soul. Such movement patterns as those in folk dances — which were in ancient times considered sacred, and which are such in essence and effect — reflect the courses of the stars, the change of the seasons and the rhythms of life in all its phases. In this way these patterns are reinforced and strengthened both in nature and in humans.

What truth is there in stories about people who one night on the lonely heath have witnessed the fairies' round, have heard their songs and have been allowed to sit at their feast table? They fell asleep and when they awoke there was nothing but wind and dead leaves. For a brief moment, their consciousness was opened to ethereal forms, and they entered a state of clairvoyance. The elves cannot stand bright sunlight and therefore appear only in the evening and hold their feasts at night by starlight and the rays of the moon; by day, they generally seek the shadow of large plant leaves and trees. To the clairvoyant, they are always visible.

14. Tree Spirits

While the elves of herbaceous plants generally have a female appearance or sometimes that of small boys, those of the large bushes and trees have a male form — in fact, just like the faun in the illustrations of the ancient Greeks. They live at the crown of the tree and can go no further than the roots of the tree stretch. In a wood, where the trees are so close to each other that the root systems of the one intertwine with those of its neighbours, a tree faun can of course move about the whole wood. He in fact moves by means of the magnetism emanating from the roots — just as a trolley bus cannot let go of its wire.

In trees of a more female nature, such as the lime, the birch and the alder, the tree spirit or dryad (called an *inwiedie* in the Edda) has a female form.

They are the external soul of the tree up to the time when a tree lifts itself a little beyond the group soul of its kind and takes on rather more individual characteristics — then, the tree elf retreats inside the trunk and becomes an internal soul or tree spirit. The result is what Tolkien in his book *The Lord of the Rings* calls an 'ent' — a tree which is *somebody*. This occurs gradually, at a relatively ripe age.

Trees and Humans

An individualised tree of this kind emanates great power, which is observed by humans unless their minds are too blunted. In a wood, the atmosphere can be so solemn that a walker falls silent and hardly dares breathe. These mighty trees have through the ages been a refuge to us when we were in need. As of old, two lime trees were planted with each new farmhouse, and an alder in the back garden. Or, in the case of the Saxon farmers, oaks around the house. On sickness, in labour, or in pain, people sought the tree and embraced the trunk. They then felt its comfort flow warmly over them. Young people with the smart of love sought out the lime; men who went to war, the oak; people who had become lost in problems of the mind, the birch — because the lime represents the force of Venus, the oak that of Mars and Jupiter, the birch that of Mercury.

All too often, humans are the deceivers and enemies of trees. In areas with an old culture (from the heart), woodcutters ask the tree for forgiveness before they cut it down. They also leave the tree faun time to move to a young tree, if there is one in the neigh-bourhood, and help him to do so by carrying him hither.

Like cows, horses or sheep taken to the slaughter-house, trees feel their death by cutting in advance and are then very sad. Since tree spirits live outside time, like all natural creatures, they know the future just as well as the past.

In some areas, it was the custom for the woodcutter to make the sign of a cross above the stump immediately after the fall of the trunk, in order to confine the spirit in it. The stump would then again send out shoots, but its mutilation remained something ter-rible to it. Even the cutting of the trunk in the sawmill is still felt as a great pain by the tree.

Sensitive persons find it terrible to see a tree felled when it is still in the prime of its life. Amongst its fellow trees, there is some-times a feeling of vengeance towards the murderer. The chopping down of sound trees is a misdeed which rebounds on those respon-sible for it.

When the Roman general Julius Caesar and his soldiers want-ed to penetrate the southern coast of Gaul (now France) where, in those days, there were still extensive oak forests, no one dared lift a hatchet. They hesitated to touch the holy wood. Then Caesar him-self cut down the first tree. The soldiers then followed his exam-ple. Now, the South is a desert of stone, wind and baking sun, where no stream murmurs and no plant will grow.

If a tree is struck by lightning, a faun can still save its life by moving elsewhere but a tree spirit often dies with its tree. Certain types of tree attract lightning, such as willows and oaks. Elms and beeches, on the other hand, are not affected. Hence the admonitory rhyme in German:

> *Eichen und Weiden*
> *soll man meiden.*
> *Ulmen und Buchen*
> *soll man suchen.*
>
> *(Willow and Oak*
> *shall you forsake.*
> *Elm and Beech,*
> *shall ye seek.)*

The small herbaceous plants are like the hairs on the human skin. Trees on the earth's body are like the more important long hairs on the human body, such as the hair of the head. They conduct cosmic forces.

Trees and the Gods

The reciprocal action between stars, tree spirits and humans was strong in olden times and to the help and advantage of all. For that reason, the sanctuary of the star godhead was built in woods or at least within a grove of its own kind of tree. Wherever people felt the godhead was already present and active, it was given a house, a place where people could come and pray to it. The tree spirits were there as its first servants and priests. Holy actions taken in a forest temple gain enormously in strength through such cooperation.

When, therefore, the remains of a forest sanctuary are discovered in an oak wood, we know that Jupiter (Zeus, Thor) reigns there and had a temple. Poplars grew by the sanctuary of the priestess Circe on Duiveland (Holland), and she therefore served Mercury (Hermes, Woden). (Circe = Tsiertse, connected with the Dutch town of Zierik-zee.) When sleeping under a tree, we often feel a message from the tree spirit giving us comfort or wise counsel. Many saints meditated beneath a tree where they received their enlightenment. The tree can mediate both between heaven and earth and between god and human.

In the neighbourhood of ancient Chinese temples we often find gingkos, the trees with a fan-shaped leaf with a nick out of the centre, like a rare rune. Trees of this type already existed in the motherland of all of us, Mu, the enormous continent that once lay where the great Atlantic now washes round its sunken peaks.

The Occult Power of Trees

The force of the tree spirit can cure the sick, especially if it is a tree of Jupiter, because he has given us the power of healing. In small villages, including those in the Dutch province of Brabant, we can still sometimes find a 'fever tree', an oak whose branches hang full of shreds of material. These have been knotted there by people, and are pieces of the shirt or bed linen of a sick person. The healing strength of the tree passes into the shreds and from there, through the ethereal bond, to the sick person him- or herself. This is called sympathetic magic. The objects close to people bear their vibrations and remain linked with them however far away their living body may be. Power vibrations can be transmitted in this way in both directions.

If hair growth is to be promoted, some of the person's hair is applied to a fast-growing, many-branched tree, for example a poplar. A piece of the bark is pulled loose, a few hairs are placed behind it, and the bark is stuck back over them. To help cure a bad arm, an African wind-flower was once fastened to the arm with a hemp string. After having endured this for several hours a day for a few days, the arm was cured but the plant was ill. We must therefore consider whether a tree is strong enough to take on an illness without damage.

Union with Humankind

How close a tree spirit and humans are to each other is clear from the old stories in which a girl fleeing a seducer was changed in time into a tree by a friendly god. Thus, the nymph Daphne was pursued by the sun god Apollo, who was burning with love for her. She ran to the river, whose god was her father and who changed her into a laurel tree on the bank. Apollo then swore that, henceforth, laurel wreaths would crown the courageous. Of course we realise that in such cases the young girl in question is not a human but a tree nymph. Although these sometimes try to avoid humans, they do sometimes want to charm them, in order to obtain possession of their immortal spirit (as in Andersen's fairy tale *The Little Mermaid*). Through sexual union, this immortality is believed to pass to the natural creature.

In Austria, for example, people tell of how a man was troubled at night by a female natural spirit, which had entered through the keyhole. In the morning, he found a wisp of down lying on his sheet, which changed into a beautiful maiden who sat crying on his bed. He took her as his wife and lived happily with her for many years, and she gave him a number of children. However, every evening he blocked up the keyhole on the front door. One day, when he forgot to do so, the woman disappeared, leaving only a wisp of down behind, which blew away through the keyhole. She was never seen again.

However long a nymph may live together with a man, she will always remain tied to her tree. This was noticed — too late — by a man who, back in the 18th century, lived near Bydzov, married happily to a tree nymph. When he noticed that she left the house each night and went to sit by a willow near the brook, he followed her one evening and, through jealousy, felled the willow. Returning satisfied, to his dismay he found his wife dead in bed. From the willow wood, he made a cradle for his youngest child and as soon as it was placed in the cradle it fell asleep. When the child had grown older and cut pipes from the willow wood, his mother spoke and sang through them to her child.

The nymph, who is ethereal, materialises at will in order to be noticed and loved by humans. The ent women described by Tolkien will also have done so.

It is the tree nymphs much more than the tree fauns who seek contact with humans, especially the nymphs of the elder and lime. In certain areas these have special names, such as Dame Cranewhite in the elder bush. In the past, a lime was often planted where roads crossed and the lime-maiden was asked to give protection on the road. The Christian church allowed these customs to continue, but changed the names. Small statues of the Virgin were placed by the limes, and this can often still be found in Munsterland in Germany. A Virgin of this kind is really a representation of the lime maiden, in the same way that the Virgins near springs and streams represent the nixie, who live in the water.

The inner bond between humans and trees is also seen in the custom of planting a young tree as a 'birth tree' when a child is born — a pear tree for girls and an apple tree for boys. Up to a certain height, both have the same horoscope. The state of the tree then continues at all times to run parallel with that of the person. If the child, now an adult, is far away, his or her fortunes can be read from the tree. If the tree dies, people are certain that the person bound to it has died. This has many times been proven by fact.

For example, Michael F. Relley, a former member of President Franklin Delano Roosevelt's bodyguard recounts, "It was a hard blow for the President when his mother Sara Delano died in September 1947. Barely five minutes after her departure, a mighty oak fell over in the park, in calm weather and without anyone ever having detected any disease in it."

When the actress Helene von Donniges was married in a Greek Orthodox chapel on the estate of her bridegroom, the landowner Yanco von Racowitza, lightning struck one of the three trees on the hill where the chapel stood. Yanco's father had planted them there when his three sons were born. It was Yanco's tree that had fallen. The guests murmured — a bad omen. Shortly afterwards, Yanco died.

15. The Immortal Pattern

When, one morning in autumn, the last of the fiery dahlias hang down discoloured and bewildered, victims of the night frost, who among us is not down at heart? Gone are the flowers until the spring; but where have they gone to? Their coarse material forms have disappeared, but what has happened to the soul of the plants?

When little Gerda in Andersen's fairy tale *The Snow Queen* no longer found the roses in the witch's garden and no one knew what had happened to them, she opened the garden gate, whereupon an icy wind blew all around her and she went in search of the country of the Snow Queen, the kingdom of frost and ice.

So do we, too, awaken on a winter morning in our cold bedrooms and see to our astonishment the windows conjured full of the foliage of winter. Where does it come from? Is it perhaps the ethereal forms of plants which, instead of appearing in the coarse material of their summer dress, now imprint themselves in the freezing condensation on the glass panes? How can the water otherwise achieve those forms, if they are not present in the air or in the ether? The fern and leaf patterns must surely derive from the extremely finely distributed material remains of plants that once were alive. Perhaps they are present in the smoke of the coal or oil fire, since coal and oil originate from the residue of dead plants from prehistoric times. Don't these fern shapes remind us of the fern trees of the carboniferous period pictured in our school books?

When people, animals and plants lose their material shapes, their form pattern continues to exist in ethereal matter and can under certain circumstances materialise in such a way that they become visible to ordinary human eyes. The figures that tend to take solid form are those of the power lines. The rose which is faded, the beautiful woman snatched away by death, they continue in a shape so rarified that it takes up no space and can pass through material things, existing in the ethereal kingdom beyond the limitations of space and time. The pattern is immortal.

Resurrection of Plants

Throughout the centuries of Western culture, the knowledge has persisted of how these ethereal patterns can be reduced to the material, so that a form becomes visible. Called rebirth or palingenesis, this art became relegated to a scientific pastime. The shapes rise literally from their ashes and this perhaps too is the significance of the Phoenix, which sets its nest alight and arises jubilant from the flames.

When, for example, a living herb is burned, the pattern of its form remains attached to its ashes and when these are mixed with a liquid, such as water, and allowed to freeze, the form of the plant can be recognised in the ash. A plant can also be reduced in rain water and the latter distilled — the plant forms will be recognised in the green oil that remains.

Dr William Maxwell (1619-1669), a friend of the Rosicrucian Dr

Robert Fludd (1574-1637) describes the method:

Take a good quantity of rose leaves, dry them by the fire and finally make this so hot that they burn to a white ash. With ordinary water, now leach out the salts and place these in a very well sealed filter jar for three months by the fire. Then bury it for six months in manure. Then take it out again and heat it up until shapes begin to appear in the glass. Then some of it may be taken and mixed with true rose water, in order to obtain a very powerful heart medicine, useful for all hot fevers that dry out the body.

In 1790, a Prussian gamekeeper discovered that a whole pine forest could be conjured out of a glass bowl from white turpentine obtained from the turpentine tree.

Again, another source relates, "I mixed the salts of all kinds of plants and placed them in two tall jars together with a little salt of lavender. Towards the evening, I saw to my amazement tiny lavender plants rising from the water round the edge of the jars. In the morning, they had covered the base of the jars, and by warming the jars I was able to repeat this wonder for a whole week."

The famous Agrippa von Nettesheim (1486-1535) advises: "As soon as the vine-stock begins to bloom, place a generous glass container full of olive oil by it and allow the twig to hang in it with leaves and buds. It is then sealed and fastened firmly to the vine-stock to protect it from the wind. The sun must be able to shine on it fully. When the grapes have ripened in the oil, press them in a linen cloth and keep the juice in the oil. If the oil is then used in a lamp, the whole room will fill with green stems, branches and grape bunches."

Robert Boyle (1527-1691) reports that he once had good verdigris, in which many small particles of spirits of wine remained. He dissolved this and allowed the solution obtained to freeze together with snow and salt. He observed small vine-stocks in the ice.

All these resurrected plants are intangible, shadows as it were, and are ethereal patterns that have briefly become visible.

August Strindberg (1849-1912) also made tests of this kind. He allowed tartaric acid to crystalise and observed a dendrite in the form of a vine leaf. The same happened with plant sap, including gooseberry, fritillary and dahlias.

In the 20th century, the anthroposophists Luise Kolisko and Ehrenfried Pfeiffer achieved similar effects by mixing copper chloride with plant sap: the form of the plant could be recognised in the crystallisation. Also to be seen was the correspondence of the image with the crystallisation figure of a part of the human body for which the plant has long been used medically, for example the root of the greater celandine and the gall bladder (as illustrated in Wilhelm Pelikan's book *Heilpflanzenkunde*).

The Ethereal Pattern of Humans and Animals

With humans and animals it is no different than with plants. De la Warr has made a device in which a drop of human blood can be placed and kept, after which, as long as the person is alive, it is possible to determine the physical state of the person at the time the device is read. The ethereal pattern of the drop changes in the same way as that of the blood still present in the body as they remain linked. By precipitating the pattern of the blood drop in substance, it is possible to obtain the appearance of the person as a shadow. In this way, the medieval alchemists bred their miniature people — the 'homunculi'.

The ethereal pattern attaches to all components of the earthly form, even if they have been reduced to ash or been diluted a million times to make a homoeopathic tablet.

Images of anything that has ever existed in tangible form and which exists now and ever will exist are present in the ether. The ether is outside time and space and penetrates all, even the most solid substance. The pattern belonging to the ethereal world is immortal.

> Weep not for beauty that has faded
> or for loved souls that are gone.
> Everything that briefly appeared on earth,
> exists and lives on. One day it
> will again appear on earth
> because every creature is merely an image
> of a part of the great body
> called the Cosmos and of which we people
> are the living cells.

16. Plants as Healers of the Human Soul

Plants, in the form of medicinal herbs, influence not only the human body but also the soul. This is not so much due to the substances of which the plant body consists but to the forces and radiations proceeding from the plant. The ethereal acts on the ethereal, soul works upon soul.

We have already seen how a sprig of herbs hung up in the home can drive out all evil, by destroying both the germs of the disease and the vibrations of black magic. The scent and aroma of a plant, which affect body and soul alike, lie between substance and vibration. The smell of a lily of the valley, for example, strengthens the heart and also human courage. The scent of roses strengthens the human ethereal field and brings joy into the soul.

Carry a strongly radiant plant around with you and if the strength of someone else's soul has also been added to it by blessing, it becomes an amulet that turns away evil.

In earlier times, the roots of plants were sold and carried as amulets against certain diseases, infections and influences. These are analogous to amulets of metal or precious stones. All have a radiation. A sliver of zinc hung by a small cord round the neck of an asthmatic can cure bronchial and nervous asthma through the calming effect of the zinc. A zinc-containing herb could also be made into an amulet.

The Power of Homoeopathic Dilution

The finer the regions of the soul that are to be affected, the more must stones, metals or plants be divided and diluted in order to free the force vibrations from the restrictions of the material form.

This is a basic principle of homoeopathy. In very high potencies, diluted or ground down and shaken, for example in a ratio of 1 to a figure composed of a 1 and 200 zeros, referred to as D200 (D stands for dilution), nothing further can be traced of the active substance by chemical investigation, but the force caught up in the substance has been freed by dilution and taken up into the cosmic life force by shaking. In a dilution of 1 million (D6), many healing substances have the same dilution they have in the human blood, so that they can be taken up directly by it. Refined to D200, the power reaches the vibration speed of the soul.

The scent and radiation of plant parts are also dilutions that have an immediate effect on the human ethereal force field or ethereal body (bioplasma). It is here that the pattern of a person's whole life process lies, a pattern expressed on all planes and levels, in the circumstances of both the life of the soul and the body. Since homoeopathically diluted natural substances derived from the plant, animal or mineral kingdom affect the living body, they are implicitly medicines for the soul and body alike and at the same time act as magic potions that purify, cure or rectify our surroundings, and so affect our circumstances, our fate. They attract good forces and repel the bad.

Famous homoeopathic physicians such as the American Nash and the Frenchman Gallavardin used specifics in D2000 and D6000. Administered against a disease of the body, they likewise change one's nature, soul and character. Through them, people are cured of alcoholism, irascibility, obtuseness, sex fixations and the like. It is just a matter of the physician or healer, by intuition or experience, recognising what specifically fits the pattern of the person at that moment.

Further Examples

Take for example, the well known substance Belladonna (deadly nightshade, *Atropa belladonna*, highly toxic). Drops of the tincture are placed in the eyes in order to enlarge the pupil so, for a time, to become a beautiful woman — a 'bella donna'. In D3 (1 in a 1000) it is an excellent cure against many ailments, from bed-wetting to the onset of dangerous infections. If, however, it is applied in D300, it acts on the particularly female tendencies of the soul, for example coquettishness and the desire that sometimes occurs after childbirth to jump from the window with the nurseling. These feelings will then disappear, as indicated in a case history by Gallavardin (in the version of his notes edited by Dr Hans Triebel, in the book *Homoeopathische Beeinflussung von Charakter, Trunksucht und Sexyaltrieb*, Haug-Verlag).

Just think of the tremendous grief and damage done in our time through the ravages of uncontrolled sexual passion in young men. The countless, terrible assaults that instil an aversion to sex in girls throughout their lives, often make an abortion necessary and sometimes lead to murder or suicide. This lack of control can be cured. And how many people are there who themselves would like to be freed of their sexual obsessions, but do not know how. And how many who masturbate who would so dearly like to be released from their addiction? Such remedies have been sought from time immemorial in cloisters and monasteries. Various herbs exist against this, including lamb's wort (*Agnus castus*), as the name already indicates. The simplest is in fact the kitchen herb marjoram (*Origanum majorana*) which, in D4, already produces this effect.

Amongst women, Platina D300, and sometimes D30, often has excellent effects. *Nux vomica*, the poison nut, is a substance very commonly used in homoeopathy. Its uses are many and it is good for people with a highly charged affective soul (moon-Uranus affliction), who by turns are in deep depression or at the summit of enthusiasm (manic depression). They are restless if their stomach has insufficient albuminous food to digest and if their soul does not obtain sufficient emotional impressions to process.

The poison nut (*Strychnos nux vomica*) is a tree with white flowers and spherical fruits which grows in Southern Asia and whose seeds are poisonous when eaten. They sharpen the senses and produce muscular spasm. In a homoeopathic dilution, D3 (i.e. 1 in 1000) and greater, since its abundance of yang force is then cut down to size, the poison nut cures such ailments as facial paralysis (one half of the face), paralysis following diphtheria, bladder spasm and bed-wetting. The seeds then in fact have a stimulating effect, particularly during weakness following serious infectious diseases and, especially, as a heart tonic.

The poison nut strengthens the ego (analogous to the heart) in overcoming disturbances in the inner feelings.

A very high potency, such as D200, need be administered once only or several times at the most, at intervals of at least two weeks, in order to render a restless and sometimes vicious person calm and friendly. What, after all, is viciousness? What makes someone flare up against a certain, hated other person; through an excess of electrical charge, which amplifies all impressions of the soul and all reactions of the soul. In a high dilution, the power of the poison nut in fact calms this electrical excess in the ethereal body (bio-plasma).

Nux vomica in a high dilution helps against jealousy, against heavy addiction to drink which leads to the abuse of wife and children, against excessive sex, sleeplessness due to disquiet, and a touchy disposition through which the whole family lives in continual fear of outbursts. It may also be given to patients against physical ailments after which they notice with surprise that the ailment has gone and, what is more, they have become a different person! This is what magic can offer.

Yet another remarkable although poisonous plant is the hemlock, *Conium maculatum*, a stately umbellifer with brown spots on its fine triple-sprung leaves. Used fresh, undiluted, this plant is extremely toxic and was therefore placed in the poisoned goblet that Socrates had to drink. Plato has described how the poison first paralyses the legs and then causes the lameness to rise until breathing is affected and death follows.

In a fairly light dilution, such as Conium D4, this poison reduces excess creative force, for example in the case of incipient cancer which occurs amongst women who take something to avoid pregnancy but still seek sexual arousal. The creative force in their womb then begins to construct cells of the embryonic kind at random, a condition which expresses itself in warts, bumps and swellings, and sometimes initially as cellulitis, inflammation of the cells of the skin.

The Dutch personal physician to the Austrian Queen Theresia discovered that this custom led to cancer.

In a very high dilution, it in fact reduces paralysis of the soul functions amongst old people and therefore prevents dementia. Gallavardin was successful with an 84-year-old woman who in her youth had been very lively and was losing all interest in her surroundings and in what was happening about her. With Conium D3000 she regained her liveliness of spirit.

In an intermediate potency, such as D30, Conium is good for swollen glands, paralysis of the nerves of the brain and spinal marrow, shaking of the hands and dizziness amongst old people.

The generally known Arnica, *Arnica montana*, can also influence the soul. Everyone knows that it grows on hilly slopes and helps in the case of a fall; both against the swellings, sprains and contusions and against the shock to the nerves that can result. It is a powerful anaesthetic and when a tooth has to be extracted, a few grains of Arnica D3 should be taken in advance and the extraction can be made quite painlessly. It can be used both externally and internally. Tincture of Arnica should be kept in every home for rubbing, diluted with water, on a sore spot.

Healers of Nerves and Soul

An injured soul can also be cured by Arnica, particularly if this is expressed in such great indifference that a person will spend the whole day sitting on a chair and reacting to nothing. A single administration of 5 grains of Arnica D200 can, however, change a person so completely that they will suddenly brim over with life. Should this become excessive, Arnica D100 may have to be given a week later in order to calm them down. The wound in the soul which had killed all interest then appears healed.

Another wonderful plant of this kind is St John's wort, *Hypericum perforatum*. It belongs to the family of Hypericaceae, reaches a height of 60 to 70 cms and used to grow abundantly on sandy soil, where it blooms on St John's day, 24 June, with golden-yellow, five-petalled flowers. If the leaves are held up to the light, they can be seen to contain spots; these are the oil glands. If the fresh flowers and leaves, slightly chopped, are placed in a glass jar with olive oil and the jar is placed sealed in the sun for two weeks, the oil will turn red and seven weeks later we have the excellent St John's wort oil, for use externally and internally against a great many ailments, particularly those affecting the nerves. Subcutaneous bleeding, with this rubbed on it, is cured remarkably quickly. It also prevents paralysis of the nerves through cold, paralysis after a stroke and nerve pains (neuralgia).

Children who find it difficult to move their arms and legs through brain damage at birth should have their limbs rubbed with it. To prevent bed-wetting, the inside of the thighs and the lower abdomen can be rubbed with it in order to activate the nerves that pass through that area, so that they give a warning when the bladder is full. The St John's wort has a close association with the sun, which gives it its great curative power, and it therefore blooms at its zenith — midsummer. Cows that have eaten St John's wort glow in the night. We can protect ourselves against sunburn by rubbing the exposed skin with St John's wort.

It is best to use this herb internally and externally at the same time. Start internally with one drop of St John's wort oil and increase this by one drop extra each day up to seven drops, and then decrease in the same way. Tea can also be taken daily of the fresh or dried herb (stalk, leaf and flower). This is good for preventing and curing exhaustion, nervous stress and melancholy (having had enough of earthly life). The St John's wort feeds and strengthens the nerves and soul. In a high solution, for example D60, it is even more effective against melancholy and neurosis. After all the sun's power gives the soul courage and self-assurance, joy of life, a positive attitude and a belief in the happy conclusion of things. People with a depressed sun in their horoscope should drink St John's wort tea daily.

We should also mention the club moss (*Lycopodium*) and Bombay nut or cashew (*Anacardium*) to which we devote a special chapter in this book in the section on plant souls. Anacardium protects the soul against possession by a disembodied spirit while Lycopodium will protect weak people, children and the elderly against dominance by parents or overbearing carers.

Many other plants will be found in homoeopathic textbooks which cure the body in a low dilution and the soul in a very high dilution. Homoeopathically diluted herbal extracts are diluted from substance to force, and as from a certain dilution act directly on the human force field, bioplasma or ethereal body, and hence on the soul. The greater the potency (= force), the longer the time to be left after application, so that the specific can work deep to the core without being disturbed. Some people wonder to what extent it is permissible for the human soul to be influenced for the good. Shouldn't we raise ourselves by our own efforts, by our own free will? In giving someone a homoeopathic medicine which changes their soul pattern, are we not depriving them of the lesson that lay in the poor state of their soul as a task for the ego?

This is an aspect of the great question — to what extent may medicaments be applied, since everything can, after all, ultimately be cured by the spirit? Shouldn't we first discover through our suffering that this is the result of a wrong attitude of the soul? In principle, yes. But our fellow human beings should help us to obtain that insight. What is therefore needed first is to talk to the person. As regards those who do not want to talk and become more and more immersed in their misery — they should be left well alone, trusting that the self-healing process of the soul will lead them to a solution. But there are also a great many cases where a helping hand (Jupiter in the horoscope) is inculcated in the life pattern of the patient as a messenger of God and such a helper is then authorised to use every suitable means. These are things that can be decided only at the point when we are faced with a particular problem and then intuition, insight and experience must determine the choice — and a prayer for the correct prompting will not come amiss.

PART 2
Plant Souls

1. The Herb Posy

At one time a posy of herbs would hang from the smoke-blackened collar-beams in every farmhouse. This was a dried bunch of beneficial herbs that had been picked during the summer. The time for doing this was St John's day (24 June), i.e. just after the longest light, because all growing things had then drunk of the full glory of the sun. Also 14 August, the eve of the Assumption, but originally Hertha's day (the Dutch 'Hartjesdag', which is still celebrated with bonfires in the old quarter of Amsterdam), Hertha or Irtha being Mother Earth. Of old, people would make their way in a long line along a spiral path up a wooded hill in order to imitate the spiral that the sun presents to our eyes: "What the gods do, people must do likewise."

At the centre of a posy of this kind there would be a sun herb: a sunflower, marigold, spikenard or mullein, or a St John's wort. Around it, the herbs of Mercury, Venus, Earth, Mars, Lucifer, Jupiter, Saturn, Uranus, Neptune and Pluto — just as the planets revolve round the sun like knights round their king, and are represented in the traditional brooch or knot of Dutch Zeeland. It is possible for anyone to find this out.*

Traditional compositions included the St John's wort posy of seven herbs, the nine-herb posy and the fifteen-herb posy.

Seven-Herb Posy

The St John's posy will certainly have had a St John's wort (*Hypericum perforatum*) at the centre and been accompanied, so it is said, by the cuckoo pint (*Yarum*), marjoram (*Origanum*), milk thistle (*Cnicus benedictus*), garlic (*Allium*), fennel (*Nigella*), pennywort

---

* See M. Uyldert *Stars, People, Herbs* (in Dutch).

(*Hydrocotyle*), asafoetida (*Excrementum diaboli* — for the air!) and scabious (*Succisa*), the initials of the Latin names or descriptions shown in brackets here combining to form the name Johannes. However, it was not because of this that they were used but because of their medicinal radiation which wards off both evil thoughts and intentions and the germs of disease. Negative etheric images create harmful bacilli, bacteria or viruses. Transmuting them is a better option.

Nine-herb Posy

The nine-herb posy was burned towards mid-winter on glowing charcoal in a copper pan (a bed warmer) with a long handle, with which the farmer would proceed through the house and stables to purify them on the four holy incense nights, the eves of St Thomas, Christmas, New Year's Day and Epiphany. This posy had to be picked on the 14 August before sunset and without using a knife since iron removes its power. At the centre was the spikehead or 'Wodan's head'. (Wodan is Mercury, governing, amongst other things, the air passages, breath and speech, and the root of the spikehead is one of the best expectorants for bronchitis and bronchial asthma; part must be boiled and part allowed to soak in water and the two extracts mixed and drunk.) The spikehead has a golden yellow flower (sun). Wodan/Mercury is the chief god in northern Europe (the pole of thought) while Thor/Jupiter is the chief god in the south (the pole of life). Arranged roundabout were agrimony, valerian, wormwood, balm, southernwood, bitter-sweet, tansy and squinansywort. And also, sometimes, yarrow and rue.

Fifteen-herb Posy

The fifteen-herb posy had the mullein at the centre, and around it reedmace, burnet, St John's wort, harebell, scabious, caraway, spearmint, tansy and creeping cinquefoil.

These herbs had to be entwined three times with the stem of bittersweet. They were also infused, and the extract added to the bath water for a 'witches bath', i.e. a bath for calming a hysterical woman, who had to be kept lying in it for three and a half hours.

Unlike the other herbs, bittersweet is poisonous. In the southern part of the Netherlands it is called 'fairy runner'; a magical herb, belonging to the *Solanaceae* family, which also includes the deadly nightshade, tobacco, the tomato and the potato.

The composition taken need not, in fact, be precisely that mentioned above. In any event, it is a good custom to have a few cleansing herbs purify your house during the winter, dried and possibly placed on glowing charcoal.

They can be put on the fire in a metal jam jar lid, for example. Particularly suitable against epidemic flu are sage, thyme, camomile, marjoram, juniper berries, lavender, rosemary, and possibly some church incense (resin drops or olibanum). They drive away germs and demons (images of the human soul, assumptions, desires, feelings, thoughts and ambitions that have taken on an independent existence). The flame of a candle, preferably of a beeswax candle,* does the same.

If your child has pains in the night or a frightening dream, light a candle and burn a little camomile and sage. If it happens frequently, infuse a few leaves of sage in hot milk and let the child drink some of it before he or she goes to bed. For continuous harmony in your home, hang a posy that suits your horoscope above your bed and/or in your living room.

2. The Heathland Community

"On the great and silent heath, the shepherd wends his lonely way while his white and woolly flock is guarded by his faithful dog."

So we sang in the past, but this great and silent heath no longer exists in the Netherlands, apart from a few fragments. The wattle huts have disappeared as have the sheepfolds, and the dark Speulder wood, in which the hamlet of Drie lay hidden, has been chopped down. On the Lüneburger Heide, in north-west Germany, the shepherd and his sheep can still be seen, as can the old Saxon farms, sheltered by ancient oaks — the trees of Thor. Here, too,

---

* Beeswax candles can be obtained in various sizes and at various prices from specialist candle makers.

from a hillock we can see the juniper berry bushes standing in groups, climbing the slopes like soldiers suddenly enchanted into immobility. A mysterious and independent tree, appearing only in lonely spots, its dark-blue berry ripens slowly, over two years, and only then is its power fully concentrated, cleansing the human blood of acids. The berry, dried and kept through the winter, is chewed and the resinous taste tells of its life on the moors, harsh and rigorous on the dry ground, with the storm blowing above.

Anything that grows there is usually dry and woody, but also strong and tough. Saturn and Mars live here on the bushy moors, the bell heather and the cross-leaved heath, the blue and red bilberry, the cranberry, and the Scots pine with its tremendous life force, shooting upwards at half a metre a year. I have seen the cross-leaved heath near Render Klippen on the Veluwe. When Blaricum in the Gooi was still a sleepy country village with sandy tracks, where the rain puddles shone in the grooves left by the milk carts and the wind blowing in from the Zuiderzee conjured waves in the shifting sand of the heathland, the wild rose and sour bramble still grew there.

Great tracts of clouds drift over the lonely moors, and the shepherd, knitting mittens as he goes, tells his strange tales and stories to the child by his side, and — lie down quickly, here comes Wodan! The ancient warrior, who gave speech to humans and causes the leaves to whisper, storms through the air above the second-sighted man with his flock and dog, greeting the birches which enliven the heath in their groups of three. The birch is charming and seeks the sun on the wide moors. Because it bends with the wind it suffers no harm. It loves the air and the space around it. It is hardly of this earth — its roots spread horizontally, quite loose in the ground.

In spring, the tough woody bushes of the golden yellow gorse flow over the heathland path.

All in all, they form the heathland community: the dry ground with its purple mantle of honey-scented heather, the fir wood with its bilberries, the juniper berry, the groups of birches and, in the autumn, the many toadstools. The bell heather by the pool, with the creeping willow, the cross-leaved heath with its blackberries loved by the cows, the cowberry and the cranberry. The roses and the brambles. The gorse, the white flints, the loneliness and the wind with its old stories, the fleeting clouds. The sheep, that nibble up every young shoot and so safeguard the heather, which would otherwise be lost in the forest. And in the early autumn, when the heath is in bloom, the humming of the bees which come to fetch the honey, flying to and fro between the hives which the beekeeper has put round the edge of the heath during the night. The sun, the silence, the humming.

Imbalance and Decay

As soon as one of the members of the community drops out, the harmony is broken and decay commences. If the shepherd disappears (even despite his subsidy), merely because too many hikers appear, frightening the sheep, then more and more firs and oaks spring up which are in turn chopped down. What is left is a wan-coloured space, where the heathland plants do not grow and no toadstools appear. The soil deteriorates for lack of sheep's manure. The ground water level drops, the pool dries up, the creeping willow and bell heather disappear. The juniper berry withdraws for fear of humans. The wood becomes very dry, the bilberries less juicy and steadily scarcer.

The cowberry and cranberry are no longer seen. The heathland is impoverished. The ling loses height, it feels sad and forlorn. The bell heather disappears. The firs and birches continue. But the damp moss at their feet dries up and the red and brown heads appear in it less and less, and after a few wet September days the toadstools are gone. As soon as the woodcutters get busy, the gnomes appear to be angry and their secret paths lie lonely and exposed. The gorse dies off, the rose has departed.

More and more people flatten the paths, tear up the ling, leave rubbish behind. The heath becomes dry, it can no longer recuperate. And now the grass becomes more daring, its seed attaching to the shoes of the people; it starts to germinate and push back the grieving heath, it produces beige patches in the purple, increasing steadily. The atmosphere becomes thin and weak. The protectors are now elsewhere.

Humans and the dry grass accompanying them create the steppe. Then comes a great crisis — the death of humankind, which has felled its best friends, the trees, and so chased off the good spirits of nature.

For a long age there will be nothing.

The housing estates rot, no aircraft drone in the air. The earth is stricken by drenching showers and burning sun. Only the seeds sleeping deep below the ground live on.

Harmony and Regeneration

And then, one day when penance has been done, everything will be silent. Two people will appear across the empty heath, singing from afar. They will dig out a hollow with their hands, in order to have a long, deep, warm sleep there during the winter. In the summer, they will breathe the sun-drenched air and be outside on the earth, day and night. Then, through their love, the seeds that lie in wait will germinate.

The fir will grow again and between its roots the bushy ling will again venture forth. An acorn will sprout and mighty oaks will once again protect thankful people. Humans will live for the scent of the fir when the sun shines on it and will share the toadstools with the squirrel. The heath community will return, sheep will fertilise the soil and give their wool to humankind. The heather will again become green and purple and scented, the bees will buzz once more. The wild rose will bloom and not be torn down. Humankind will have changed.

And so everything will begin again, but better.

The Ericaceae

The family of the *ericaceae* is just like the people whose traditional home is the heath: dour, dry, strong and tough. The farmers of the Veluwe, laboriously tilling the poor soil, were always dressed in black, taciturn and imbued with a sense of original sin. The husband cut the squares of peat with which the half-underground hut was covered, the wife sat in the heather with their child, cooking a rye porridge on the petroleum stove and fetching water from the 'bottle', the heath pool — in fact exactly as campers live now. But between the one and the other there is a whole history of human error: a misunderstanding of money.

The heathland plants, too, are strong and tough, dry and woody, the leaf being sere, sometimes leathery, designed for long periods of food shortage. Governed by Mars, they are sharp fighters of disease and governed by Saturn they are granted a long and sober life. All are good against inflammations (Mars) and rheumatism (Saturn). They spur on the digestive glands to extract more from food, and so also stimulate the pancreas and cure diabetes. Their coagulating power (Saturn) stops diarrhoea and other excessive flux by its drying effect. The flower of the ling, bilberry and related plants is little to look at: no luxury, no Venus! The Mars power comes forcefully to grips with the Venus organs— kidneys and bladder — destroying infection.

Ling (Calluna vulgaris)

Rich in the rather sharp but powerful heath honey. Tea from the flowering herb has an antiseptic, cleansing hydrogogue, coagulant and calming effect, and helps to cure rheumatism and inflammation of the urinary tracts. The French call it *bruyère* and we also call it heather (the heather grows on the heath, but these two words are sometimes interchanged).

Bell Heather (Erica cinerea)

This grows where the soil is wet and has large flowers, like red bubbles or bells. Its tea has a cooling effect on fevers.

Bilberry (Vaccinium myrtillus L.)

Low bushes cover the bottom of fir trees in abundance, and proliferate on the Veluwe, where children collect the berries for the trade, though these are juicier and larger in the Alps. The juice pressed from the dark blue berries cures diarrhoea and is sold in bottles as Medicinal Bilberry juice. It deposits a coating of its protective blue colouring on inflamed membrane and so also cures inflammation of the mouth (frequent rinsing!).

Still more effective than the juice is a decoction of the dried berries, which are obtainable everywhere abroad and are much cheaper than the juice.

Cowberry (Vaccinium vitis idaei L.)

The vine of the hill of Ida — it is more common in the mountains than on flat ground and its effect is strongly antiseptic. For example, the finely chopped fresh berries can be placed on cancerous swellings, from which they extract the evil. A tea against rheumatism can be infused from leaf and flower. Here, they can be bought in tins for adding to meat dishes, the impurities of which they neutralise. The taste is sourish and rather sharp.

Cranberry (Vaccinium oxycoccus)

With its lighter red flower and red berry, this grows on peaty soil. It has a cooling effect on fevers.

Giant Cranberry (Vaccinium macrocarpon)

This has long grown on the Dutch islands of Texel, Vlieland and Terschelling where it is also cultivated. The large red berries are also eaten with meat dishes. Dried, they can be kept for a lengthy period as vitamin-rich winter food. In the Scandinavian countries, they are a traditional standby in the long vegetable-less winter.

Northern Bilberry (Vaccinium uliginosum)

These berries of the moors must not be eaten as they are narcotic but they can cure certain inflammations (cystitis, gastritis and enteritis).

Bearberry (Arctostaphy uva ursi)

Rich in vitamin C, this is the most antiseptic of all berries. Tea can be infused from the leaf (45g in 300 ml of boiling water) and one spoonful of this taken five times daily for inflammation of the bladder, diabetes and other disturbances of the pancreas, leucorrhoea, purulent inflammation of the kidneys and incontinence. A remarkably good medicament! It is hardly to be found in this country, but grows above the tree line in the far north, a hardy plant which works hard but effectively.

This family also includes shrubs that in Britain are known only as ornamental bushes in the cultivated form — the azalea and rhododendron (the leathery leaves of Saturn), related to the alpine rose of the mountain slopes. They grow in the shade on all saturnine (i.e. poor), acidic soil admirably furnishing the wild gardens of old country houses with their enormous riches of blooms in May: lilac, red, white and pale or salmon pink. A homoeopathic medicine is prepared from the leaves of the Siberian yellow alpine rose: Rhododendron Chrysanthemum D2. This acts against rheumatism and arthritis and against inflammation of the testicles and prostate.

American Laurel (Kalmia latifolia)

An ornamental bush with pink flowers like sugar loaves. A homoeopathic medicine is made of the leaf (D2 or D3) against rheumatism, arthritis and affectations of the heart muscles, and also for pain in the face and other kinds of neuralgia, malfunction of the valves of the heart and heart spasm. Fresh leaves are *poisonous*.

Bog Rosemary (Ledum palustre)

This is a Baltic plant. It is a powerful medicine, the evaporated plant overcoming insects and cattle. It grows in the bog and acts against rheumatism caused by damp and on dropsy, particularly on rheumatism of the joints, and on accumulations of uric acid (chalk-stone, gout, and swellings of the heel and soles of the feet). D2 or a higher potency is taken.

This family of plants therefore suits persons with a saturnine, psoriatic system, who accumulate uric acid. The effect on them is a thorough cleansing. Only the bilberry, which itself produces an excess of acidity, should be used merely as a gland stimulant, a coagulant and protector of the mucous membranes.

3. Silverweed

The silverweed (*Potentilla anserina*) is a small plant crawling across the soil by means of runners. It has five small flowers, arranged along a stem and is similar to close relatives, the creeping cinquefoil (*Potentilla reptans*) and tormentil (*tormentilla*), but differs from them through its pinnate leaves which are silver-grey on the underside and have a dentated edge. The small leaves are not paired and sometimes have the beginnings of a tiny leaf on their underside. The plant has fine hairs all over. The potentillas belong to the *rosaceae* and all have a coagulant, calming effect (stopping diarrhoea, haemorrhages and leucorrhoea).

The silverweed contains tannin, magnesium and something paraffin-like. It is a great spasmolytic, i.e. calms spasm, the sudden gripes of Uranus, particularly those of the womb and the lower opening of the stomach. Silverweed is useful for spasm of the womb and painful menstruation (dysmenorrhoea), inflammation of the lining of the stomach (gastritis) and of the duodenum, and stomach or duodenal ulcer, over-acidity of the stomach (Uranus-Moon) and all kinds of stomach upsets of people with an unstable Moon (vegetative nerve system), and chronic complaints of the intestines. It is useful, too, against sural spasm (Aquarius). The fresh root can be chewed against toothache.

The fresh or dried herb as a whole can be infused in hot milk for five minutes. The milk should be drunk for spasm of the stomach and intestines. Tea from the leaves may be drunk against diarrhoea, haemorrhage, stone, inflammation of the kidneys and bladder, jaundice and dropsy, arthritis, scurvy and internal injury and pain.

The original tincture, *Potentilla anserina,* is taken homoeopathically, five drops in water three times daily.

In the past, the herb was fed to young geese, hence the name *anserina.*

4. Ground-Ivy

The ground-ivy (*Glechoma hederacea*) is a pleasant labiate creeping through your garden, putting down rootlets here and there in order to gain hold and raising a few flower stalks with purple labiate flowers between the crenated round leaves. It seeks out those who have a lympathic, scrofulous system, often with their lymph glands swollen through over-tiredness. It drives mucus from the air passages and water from the kidneys. It contains tannin which contracts and strengthens the over-wet membranes. Thus it can better withstand irritation and foreign bacteria, protecting the intestines against mucous and diarrhoea and the air passages against chronic catarrh. It promotes excretion of fluids from the glands and is therefore an aid to digestion, strengthening the heart and liver through its magnesium, cleansing the skin and reinvigorating through its aroma.

Ground-ivy contains much saltpetre potassium, which combats inflammation. A tea from it can be used as a rinse or drunk for toothache, and its fresh leaf can be chewed. This herb often grows next to the stinging nettle and when stung by the latter, we need only crush a leaf of ground-ivy and place it on the burning spot and the pain is gone. It is similarly effective on wounds and sores. A poultice can also be made of the tea or fresh juice, or dilute tincture. The tincture can even be made in the summer for use in the winter — the fresh juice is mixed with an equal quantity of alcohol, allowed to stand two weeks in the sun, properly sealed, and then sieved through a cloth and kept cool. Thin it with water for internal or external use. The fresh juice with goat's milk is a specific against TB. Tea and juice may be given for asthma, bronchitis and coughing blood.

Throughout the summer, slice the fresh herb in salads and soups. Ground-ivy is rich in vitamin C, tannin, resin, wax, gum, sugar, oil, salts and acids — a good tonic for the blood! A little strong ground-ivy tea in the bath helps with sciatica, bladder stone and kidney stone. Tea for drinking: 100g on half a litre of boiling water.

Ground-ivy has been venerated from ancient times as the sacred herb of Thor or Jupiter; in Germanic antiquity, it would be worn in wreaths on the head during ceremonies on the dewy grass on summer nights.

Ground-ivy can be picked fresh virtually the whole year through and is at its most effective when fresh (vitamin C). House-painters and printers, always exposed to lead poisoning, and those who travel the motorways who are exposed to the exhaust gases of their neighbours would do well to eat a little fresh ground-ivy each day in order to excrete the lead from the kidneys. Drops of the fresh juice were formerly introduced into the ears against singing noises. Sniffed, the juice can cure headache. Cold tea from fresh ground-ivy is bitter and stimulates the appetite!

To sum up all the good effects of ground-ivy once again, particularly in the form of the fresh juice or tea from the fresh herb:

Ground-ivy deacidifies, it dissolves tartar., dental scale and kettle scale, clarifies beer (for which it was used in the past, before hops were introduced), cleans the air passages, liver and kidneys and cures ulceration of these; it settles internal disorders—colic, jaundice (together with wormwood), and all sores, tumours and festering in that quarter; it dissolves kidney stone, reduces toothache if the mouth is rinsed with tea of ground-ivy and tansy; ground-ivy tea on a piece of cotton-wool in a sore ear soothes the pain.

Accept it with gratitude.

5. Lady's Mantle

The lady's mantle (*Alchemilla vulgaris*) belongs to the family of *rosaceae* and is an unusual plant which in both the position and shape of its leaves displays something clearly protective. This leaf, shaped like a mantle, a shoulder wrap with seven points in which the nerves lie like folds, bears a dewdrop at its centre early in the morning, because it spreads itself out like a dish. In times past the dew was collected by alchemists on glass plates to be used in their alchemical processes. Hence the name *alchemilla*.

Wherever the stem branches, a leaf of this kind carefully encircles the branching point, while the stem of the leaf itself again encircles the stalk with a sheath. Everything about this plant is embracing, cherishing and protective. In essence it is just like a womb. According to the doctrine of signatures, this is what it must then be good for, which is in fact the case — its astringent properties qualify it as a tea for every woman who gives birth, to be taken every day for ten days after the birth; it causes the womb to contract until it has returned to its original dimensions and the woman has almost regained her maiden shape.

This astringent power is common to all *rosaceae* and these therefore give us self-control, chastity, dignity and distinction. Alchemilla as a medicinal herb is a great tonic, curing internal wounds and sores, healing ruptures, strengthening the muscles.

Poultices of the tea may be placed on ruptures and on a diseased rectum. Children with ruptures should be given a decoction of the fresh herb to drink, strengthened with the powdered, dried herb. A dessertspoonful of the powder taken daily in soup for three weeks will make a woman fertile. Haemorrhages due to weakness are staunched by alchemilla.

The lady's mantle produces fine yellow-green florets in 'final umbels'. Yellow-green is the colour of the sign Cancer, the crab (from 21 June to 21 July, midsummer), which the sun enters just when these florets have opened. It is, therefore, a plant that all Cancers should have in their garden and whose flower and leaf they should infuse in a mixed herbal tea, whenever necessary.

Its effect is detergent and deacidulant, since it contains magnesium and salicylic acid; it draws water from the kidneys, cools and mollifies, staunches bleeding, heals wounds and strengthens the stomach. Because of the shape of its leaf it is sometimes called 'lion's foot' and it in fact blooms when the sun has entered Leo, from 21 July to 21 August.

6. Marigold

The marigold (*Calendula officinalis*) with its cheerful orange flowers decorates country gardens and spreads wild on rubbish and refuse dumps. It is a plant of life and death and the conflict between them. Sown in the garden, it grows rapidly through tremendous moon force. A tendency towards cleavage is clear from the leaf, which follows the stem for some length the way a mother forms a bond with her child. But the strong moon force is kept in balance by the sun force because the flower is a true sun, a centre point with emanations, a true composite. The seed is not formed at the centre of the flower but at the ends. The orange colour, which belongs to Jupiter, points to its creative capabilities (*officinalis*).

The ointment of marigold, calendula salve, is not so much used for ordinary accidental wounds — arnica is better for this — but rather for dirty wounds, with inflammation and suppuration and on cancerous wounds and swellings that emit a bad smell. Nor, indeed, is the smell of the marigold pleasant. Using its moon force, the marigold creates new cells which must replace those damaged and lost. But with its sun force, it creates a plan for new structures, a pattern for making better, healthier cells.

It cleanses at the same time. Tea from the petals may be used for washing wounds and helps to remove pus and inflammation products. Inflammation itself is a purifying fire, lit by the ego. The ego says: we shall start a new life; the old member and the spoiled pattern in the soul are removed from the subconscious. Away with negative thoughts!

This is the subtle action of the marigold on cancer patients and it is quite remarkable how this plant appears in abundance quite by itself around houses where this sickness is present. As soon as the patient has recovered or has died, the marigold disappears, its task being completed.

Tea of the petals when drunk (they may be fresh or dried) is a good curative (but it must be accompanied by the proper diet and purification of the soul).

Cancer is the result of creative forces that are kept suppressed, which cannot be used in life, loving or artistic creation and which then turn inwards and proceed to build up gratuitous material forms.

But if these swellings contain poison, there must be poison foci in the soul of old, unprocessed sorrow. Then, there is too much moon and too little sun in proportion in the person. The sun-ego must be strengthened, so that it can process, understand and clear away all those moon ailments and injuries that have been sustained. The house of the soul must be cleaned and the windows thrown open, allowing the light of truth to flood in. For this we need the help of this flower of sun and moon.

The greatest curative powers are to be found in the small wild variety of marigold which grows in the vineyards in France. Generally, this herb strengthens the heart and liver, stimulates the kidneys (effective against dropsy), and expels toxins, partly through transpiration. In France, the flower buds are infused in vinegar and they are eaten pickled like capers. Also, e.g. 30 g (l oz) of juice pressed from the flowers is mixed with 3 g (0.1 oz) of powdered earthworm and taken on an empty stomach against jaundice!

Packs of the flower petals infused in water or white wine are laid on corns and swollen glands. The juice, mixed with a mild vinegar, makes a good gargle or poultice for headache or toothache. A handful of the petals can be soaked in a litre of cold water, boiled for three quarters of an hour, sieved and pressed out. Take a few sips of this every half hour.

The marigold, as a tea of the green leaves and petals, cleanses and calms, and cures inflammations, wounds and sores, particularly internal ulcers. It is taken for nausea, constipation, nervous debility and nervous upsets, and it helps with menstruation. It is particularly good for scrofulous systems.

7. Onion

The onion (*Allium cepa*) is a variety of garlic and therefore related to the common garlic, ramsons, chives, etc., all bulbous plants whose flowers sprout in globe form at the end of a tall stem. These garlics come originally from the Near East — Persia, Chaldea and also Egypt, where according to the old inscriptions they formed the daily food of those who worked to build Cheops's pyramid. Onions were also offered on altars and mummies have been found with an onion in the hand. The ancient Greeks used the onion as a medicament, combined with honey, against cramps, pain in the joints and cancerous swellings. The ancient Romans valued the onion and leek more than any tasty vegetable and as an aphrodisiac (to stimulate desire). Wherever people eat to abundance, as at wedding breakfasts and funeral feasts, we find the onion forming an essential component of the meal.

The sharp taste of the raw onion and other garlics is due to their heavy *sulphur* content, which kills harmful germs and prevents decay and fermentation in the intestine. Anyone who eats an onion a day remains healthy when others are infected by epidemic disease, as was proved in prisoner-of-war camps where Jewish prisoners, who were always able to come by onions, proved to be far less subject to infection than others. Sulphur also expels worms: eat a raw onion on an empty stomach and infuse a finely chopped onion in water over night and drink the infusion before breakfast!

An onion cut in half and placed on a small dish next to a sickbed, renewed as required, keeps the air clean and protects visitors. For migraine, ringing in the ears and rheumatic earache, half an onion or a piece of cottonwool soaked in fresh onion juice is placed behind the ear. Colds and all ailments of the throat and bronchial tubes can be cured by taking a raw onion or an onion syrup which can be prepared by slowly (three hours) boiling down a pound of sliced onion with 80 g (3 oz) of honey and 400 g (14 oz) of brown sugar and then sieving it. Take a spoonful every two hours, preferably lukewarm!

An onion emits mitogenic radiations which promote the growth of living things in its neighbourhood. This is why the onion is one of the best remedies against loss of hair and even complete baldness. Rub a juicy slice taken from an onion over the top of the head and then, if possible, sit a while in the sun. Do this daily until the result is achieved.

What, in fact, are the special features of the onion and why do we need to discuss it here? The onion is a biennial bulbous growth and during its first year, when the seed germinates, the bulb gradually forms, consisting of juicy skin layers in which the reserve food for the later plant is stored. It contains not only sulphur, which gives it its sharp taste, but also plenty of phosphorus, which makes the onion such a good item for those who work with their mind, because phosphorus feeds the brain. Also, it contains an abundance of sugar, inulin, albumen, vitamins B_1 and C and many mineral salts. When the adult bulb is harvested as an onion it cannot, of course, develop further. But if it is allowed to follow its natural course, a long hollow stalk rises from the bulb the following year and produces a ball of fine flower stems at the upper end which eventually each bear a white or lilac flower. It looks as though the bulb has changed ends! The spare food is now gradually eaten up by the plant, after which only empty skins remain.

This procedure illustrates the process of *sublimation* of life forces into consciousness in humans. The human sexual organs in fact are not only for procreation but are also the prime transformers of the earthly life force that flows into us and serve to prepare ethereal energy from it as food for the soul, so that we will be able to discover and utilise all its features and possibilities. If the soul hungers for more development, it draws those forces upwards itself. The life juices from the gonads then pass through many stages of refinement and change into forces (just as homoeopathically diluted medicinal substance is changed into medicinal force by dilution). In women, this happens quite by itself through the formation of the corpus luteum which provides the nervous system with lecithin.

When we eat an onion and so absorb phosphorus and use it for our thinking, we are therefore really following the natural development of this plant. The onion helps us to sublimate, and drives us from matter to spirit.

It is therefore wise to eat a little onion with every meal, either chopped up raw in salad or cooked to a golden-yellow together with cereals (risotto and rice, risotto and millet) and those vegetables finely braised in oil. The chopped onion is then first browned while stirred in a pan with a little hot oil, after which vegetables are added and the pan well sealed. In this way, virtually all the vitamins and other valuable substances are retained in the vegetable. The dish is particularly tasty and palatable and salt quite unnecessary. A buttered slice of rye bread with a slice of raw onion is a healthy breakfast to prepare us for great achievements.

In homoeopathy, the onion is used as a medicine against the ailments mentioned in this chapter under its name Cepa.

8. Rue

The rue (*Ruta graveolens* — herb of grace, of the family of *Rutaceae*) is a remarkable plant possessing such curative powers that in times past it was to be found in every kitchen garden. Even its appearance is exceptional, since it has flowers in groups of four with one group of five at the top. This combination of four and five points to matter (four) governed by will (five). Perhaps this is the origin of the name 'herb of grace', and of its many medicinal effects — the easing of labour, the expulsion of the child. This was the original reason why it was grown in gardens. The second reason was that it was put in the bath water of children who suffered from convulsions.

Where there is a lack of will, rue can strengthen it. The will to give birth. The will to protect oneself from overbearing impressions; a convulsion is the state of fear of a person who is stupefied, paralysed by fright. If someone 'can go no further', if they feel mentally and physically defeated (lying in bed and feeling a pain wherever they lie), then rue is given. Once upon a time, rue was diffused in wine. Even now, in southern France a kind of country wine can still be bought containing a twig of rue. In this way, the wine was deprived of its effect of allowing the body, i.e., matter, to become master of the will, and it could not cause drunkenness: *Salvia cum ruta faciunt pocula tuta*. Sage and rue infused in wine render it harmless. Rue strengthens the consciousness, the upper pole.

When the will no longer retains control over matter the result is collapse. Rue is therefore one of the best specifics against prolapse of the intestine and anus and for weakness in the muscles and joints of the legs. It is also an excellent tonic against mental stress and burning, tired eyes. If rue is taken regularly each day, mixed with a herb tea, sight will be found to be better and sharper.

Generally speaking, rue is therefore taken for weakness of the will, soul and muscles, for tiredness and stress, especially of the eyes, against convulsions in children, congestion and dizziness, palpitations, piles and prolapse and for rheumatism in the hands and feet. It particularly strengthens the membrane surrounding the bone.

Homoeopathically, it is taken as Ruta D1 or higher. For stiff joints, e.g. Ruta D30. In folk medicine, rue is taken against all kinds of poisoning — 'and drink rue against poison' says an old Dutch proverb — and against worms. It strengthens the ego against all attack. Wine rue is a special kind of rue, with a different habit and leaf form from the ordinary rue.

9. Ivy

God created humankind in his own image, the primeval pattern of creation. And also our earth and also the plant. All display the same structure: a two-pole being with a circuit of forces combining the the two poles and maintaining reciprocal contact between them. The northern hemisphere of the earth corresponds to the upper pole, the pole of thought or consciousness in the head, in humans — and to the root of the plant. The southern hemisphere of the earth corresponds to the pole of life, seated in the sexual organs of man — and to the flower of the plant. This two pole structure is also found in every country as language areas and in every people. In the Netherlands the Friesian belongs to the pole of thought and the Brabantine to the pole of life. In Belgium and Germany the same difference is to be found amongst the inhabitants and attitudes in the north and in the south (Prussian and Bavarian). And so on in every country, because the people of a country are also a living organism.

Migrations certainly occur from the one pole to the other. For example, people take plant seeds with them from the one hemisphere to the other and sow the plant in an area foreign to them. What then happens? The same as with humans. One type fits quite happily into its new surroundings, and with people of this kind the soil (the place in *space*) appeals more strongly than the blood (inheritance, origin, tradition, the place in *time*). The other type cannot adapt, like migrants who continue to speak their mother tongue at home and attempt to bring up their children in the traditions of the home country. For them, time appeals more strongly than space.

In plants we see the same phenomenon. There are those that gradually adapt and thus adjust their life rhythm to the new climate. Others stick obstinately to their old rhythm. These are the plants which, for example, flower in the winter here because they are used to this as of old, such as winter jasmine and the witch-hazel; they flower in the summer of their old mother country in the South and take no notice of the fact that here it is winter.

Remarkable in this respect is the behaviour and progress of the ivy — particularly, too, in connection with its medical application. The ivy (*Hedera helix*) that winds round trees and covers ugly walls and sheds with a thick coat of perennially green leaves blooms in November with yellow-greenish florets. It holds fast to its old flowering period — summer in the southern hemisphere — because it harks back to its mother country, Lemuria. Together with other members of the *Araliaceae* family it grew originally at the southern tip of South America and in Australia. But there it is a self-supporting tree, with pointed, egg-round leaves which here it carries only on the flowering branches. This leaf has retained the shape that belongs to the moon and to the pole of thought, and cures the corresponding ailments, namely those of the spleen, and corns on the toes. The southern hemisphere is the life pole of the globe.

Journeying to the north, its leaf changed shape to the pentangle associated with the conscious will and the human pole of thought, and this leaf cures ailments of the head — of the ear, mouth, eye and forehead (sinusitis). It also changed its attitude from firm to creeping due to its lack of life force. Since this pentangular form serves the pole of thought and self-control (Saturn), it also protects against drunkenness. Dionysus was wreathed in vine and ivy and the ivy still climbs up the outside of many old English inns. It imparts will and endurance — in other words, perseverance!

The effect of the entire plant is astringent, germicidal, vermifuge, artery-narrowing (creating a balance with artery-diluent wine), sudorific and emmenagogic. The egg-shaped leaves crushed finely in vinegar and rose water are placed on the temples and forehead to calm excitement and rage. The pentangular leaves, pressed out and the juice mixed with oil, cure earache. The juice can also be used to dye the hair black. An extract from the flowers helps against dysentery. Chopped fresh leaves may be made into a poultice against sciatica. The sticky juice from a mature stem can be used to get rid of unwanted hair. Boiled leaves are placed on burns and, on top of them, a poultice of the water they were boiled in. Even plague is combated by drinking thirty berries dried and powdered in a glass of white wine — the patient will then sweat heavily, so should be well covered.

The leaf is infused in water as an eye-wash for man and animal. Crushed and soaked in salt vinegar, it may be tied to a corn which can then be pulled from the toe. Tea made from the pentangular leaf is drunk for mucous catarrh, jaundice and dropsy. Tincture and pills are also made from the ivy leaf. Worsted trousers and skirts that have acquired a shine can be pressed using a cloth soaked in ivy tea and wrung out. An ivy leaf in the wash makes ink and fruit spots disappear. The berries, which the birds love cannot be digested by man.

A cutting from a flowering branch will grow into a sturdy tree retaining the egg-shaped leaf. This type needs a great deal of sun, as in the mother country. The northerly, five-cornered type prefers the shade and is truly saturnine — with its leathery leaf it withstands dark and winter cold.

10. Monk's Hood

Correspondence of Character

People and plants often show similarities of character. Two great
forces — centrifugal force and, in the reverse direction, centripetal
force — act in both humans and plants. If they are in balance they
are not noticed. But if the centrifugal force predominates, this is
called the 'extrovert' type and if the centripetal force is stronger,
this type is called the 'introvert'.

Extrovert people and plants open up towards their surroundings, radiate outwards, impressing themselves on their environment and attempting to influence it in order to express themselves.
For example, creative artists, businesspeople and advertisers, edu-
cationalists and the like amongst people. Amongst plants, we find
those with wide-open flowers: the sunflower, marigold, rose, daisy
and silverweed. They give an impression of merriment, love of life
and sometimes naivety.

Introvert people turn inwards, away from their surroundings.
They process their impressions in silence and depth and oppose
any strong influences from outside — for example, poets, philoso-
phers, hermits meditating in solitude. Amongst the plants there
are those with flowers that have created a closed form by extension of their petals, for example into a bell contemplating the earth:
harebell, lily of the valley and the diagonally drooped foxglove.
Alternatively, they may have a twin-lipped shape, such as the labi-
ates and the antirrhinums or the garden plants larkspur and
monk's hood. They give an impression of meditation and often
melancholy. Introvert people, similarly, often let their heads hang.

Plants of this kind seem serious and sometimes wise. Extroverts
are often sun or moon flowers, introverts often Saturn flowers. The
two-lipped flowers are analogous to split personalities, whose pole
of thought and pole of life each live a separate life in competition
with each other. They are hiding a secret, repressed sorrow that is
nobody else's business. Just consider the snapdragon, dead nettle
and horehound.

The refined flower-shapes of aconite, larkspur and monk's hood
have something aristocratic about them, a saturnine centuries-old
self-discipline that has led to perfection. They have passed through

all the plant possibilities and stand on the threshold of the animal kingdom. The dark purple helmet-shaped flower of the monk's hood (*Aconitum napellus*) seems almost neurotic; established on the sorrow that may not be talked about, gazing sombrely and distilling poison from negative experience. A poison or alkaloid of this kind is albumen, which is converted into a substance that can serve as a carrier of feelings and emotions. With it, the plant reaches for the animal, astral, emotional life, brought about by the absorption of sensory impressions.

The monk's hood makes us think of a monk who has pulled his hood over his head to protect himself against a surfeit of impressions, in order first to digest what he has taken in deep within himself. He needs time (Saturn), and so, in the autumn when his mortal shape perishes, makes a second root which swells and retains what is so far undigested, and from which next year a new form will grow.

Remedial Power

When a preparation is made from this flower it is very like a prepared trigeminus, the three-branched nerve in the human body which spreads out from the neck across the face and skull. Now, there are introvert people who after having absorbed many impressions like to withdraw into themselves in order to digest them peacefully but who are kept from doing so by too busy a life. They then sometimes feel pain in this nerve — trigeminal neuralgia. It is extremely painful and can be brought about quite suddenly by a north-easterly wind, as an analogy of the tension between Mars (work) and Saturn (withdrawal) in their horoscope. The icy north wind comes from Saturn; the easterly wind, dry and cold, from Mars. The pain is at its worst at night, when Saturn reigns. The appropriate medicine is then the dilute poison of the monk's hood: the homoeopathic substance Aconitum D3, a frequently used nervine.

Taking this, the patient must be kept warm and remain alone, free from new impressions, because the life of the soul has been too busily occupied and has so acted on the body. The astral tormented the vegetative. This can also be noticed in a sharpening of all senses: every noise disturbs, bright lights cannot be tolerated, food appears to have all kinds of suspicious smells, and this may be accompanied by sciatica pains, colonic catarrh or bronchial trouble, sore throat and dry fever. Rest returns everything to its proper place. If the surroundings deny such rest, people defend themselves by irritability and aggression and, indeed, a fit of temper can have a curative effect.

11. Houseleek

When, as a child, I lived in the country village of Laren in Gooi in the Netherlands, I used to see a plant growing in the old, moss-covered reed roofs of the farms which carried a bunch of fat, fleshy leaves. It appeared incredible that it could live on so little soil. It was called 'houseleek' or 'sengreen' and was honoured because it turned away lightning. Charlemagne ordered every head of household to place one on the roof of his house. The plant was sacred to Thor or Jupiter and hence its old name 'Jupiter's beard'; in French it is called *joubarde des toits*, in Italian *barba di Giove* and in Latin its (botanical) name is *Sempervivum tectorum*, i.e. always living on the roof.

Medical Properties

Houseleek contains a great deal of stored up water with mucus, chalk, malic acid, tannic acid, resin and formic acid. And it does not just stand there to keep away the lightning but, as a true Jupiter plant, is medicinal in many aspects: as a refrigerant and febrifuge, astringent, purgative and alterative, diuretic, styptic and anti-spasmodic. The fresh juice cures some eczemas, warts and skin inflammations and damage, corns and freckles. Tea of the leaves helps with septic throats, bronchitis and mouth ailments. Furthermore, the juice has the special effect of clearing up thecal cyst and hygroma. These appear at the knee, heel, toe or wrist when fluid forced from the joint after a shock, for example through a fall, becomes ossified (a Saturn affliction).

Natural remedies against this are *external*: placing a fresh leaf of comfrey (*Symphytum officinale*) on the spot, or a pack of tea of cornflower or of the crushed leaf of houseleek. *Internally*, Symphytum D2 can be taken or hom. benzoic acid. Alternatively large quantities of fresh cranberries can be eaten.

I was recently again struck by the fact that what we need is generally brought to us by Providence. A girl had suffered for some time with a hygroma of the knee. After a number of medicines had had no effect, and the parents would not let it be operated on, I discovered in an old book that the fresh juice of the houseleek might be right for this. When I told them so the mother said, "This plant has grown for years in our yard but we cleared it away to keep the place tidy." Now, after some hunting in the neighbourhood, another houseleek was found and now that the swelling on the knee is being treated with fresh juice each day large ridges can be felt appearing in the lump. The body is breaking it down!

The psychosomatic link appeared to be as follows. The girl was the saturnine type, a good high school pupil who had spent a great deal of time and energy on her school work and thus had worn out her life pole, which began to become deficient. More manual work, physical games, company and a good healthy diet are indicated as a therapy, in order to balance the predominant tendency to abstraction, drying up and hardening. What is the point of removing the *result* of an unbalanced state, i.e., the swelling, by operation, if the condition itself is not changed?

The Nature of Houseleek

The characteristic of houseleek and aloe (better known as a house plant, the larger kind growing in tubs in the garden) is to store up water in its leaves, which are fleshy and swollen for this purpose. As a result, these plants can continue to live indefinitely on hard, dry subsoil, such as a roof tile, slate or shingle, without receiving much water. They draw on their reserve which is topped up again as soon as it rains — in just the same way as a Cancer type amongst people tends to keep house: always a ready store of foodstuffs in the larder!

These kinds of people store their water, i.e. the feelings in the soul, in an enormous reservoir of emotional memories. They are too shy to bring them out, except when acting on stage. People of this kind are therefore related to the houseleek, aloe and other so-called succulents. They are also prone to falling ill because of the bottled up feelings which are not understood, accepted or valued by their environment — and since they cannot be expressed outwardly are expressed inwardly, creating swellings, cysts and the like within the body. These people's surroundings are too unsafe and hard for their soul. Often they succumb and repress their feelings and their longing for a response.

12. Aloe

The aloe (*Aloe socodrina Lam*) has long, pointed, very fleshy leaves which eventually bear small teeth along the edge. They are grown in flowerpots and are given little water.

Of old, the bitter juice of the aloe leaves was used for internal ailments and for congestion in the pelvic area generally (the plant, too, is congested!). Homoeopathically, Aloe D2 to D6 is administered for swollen liver, diarrhoea, bleeding from the womb and bleeding piles; aloe pills (two before going to bed) are a laxative. Aloe promotes menstruation, consciousness and the expression of a feeling (crying fits while taking it). Do *not* take it during pregnancy, of course, as it could lead to miscarriage; nor in the case of boils. Aloe is purgative and tonic, clears the gall bladder, strengthens the tissues, and expels parasites in the intestine (worms).

A friend of ours in what was Czechoslovakia (where school children go forward to the next class only after they have collected a quantity of wild medicinal herbs) had great success with aloe for cancerous swellings of the stomach and intestine (the patient had been given up by the doctor) and also with, for example, TB of the lungs, flu, tonsillitis, headache (resulting from wrong digestion), eczema, asthma and kidney and female ailments. Her recipe was the following.

Recipe and Prescription

The fresh leaves of plants aged 3 to 5 years and which have not been watered for three days are crushed or ground. To 300 ml (11 fl oz) of juice, add 500 g (1 lb 2 oz) of honey, 70 ml (3 fl oz) of real red wine and 10 ml (1 fl oz) of pure alcohol. Mix everything and decant into a dark bottle which is put away for five days, carefully sealed, in a cool dark place.

Then, for the first five days, give the patient one teaspoonful of this mixture three times daily, three hours before each meal. Follow this with a dessertspoonful one hour before the meal. In favourable circumstances, the cure need last only three weeks. In obstinate cases, two months. In each instance, sufficient for five days is taken from the bottle and filtered through a fine cloth. Do not administer more frequently than two months a year.

In America, the aloe is called the 'beauty plant'. Because of the astringent effect of the juice from its fleshy leaves, it can in fact be used to smooth the facial skin, so removing wrinkles from it. For this, a leaf is cut off and the cut surface is rubbed twice over the skin each day. The leaf is kept in a glass of water until the next day and a slice is then cut again from it in order to obtain a fresh, juicy surface. In Indonesia, women rub a cut leaf of this kind across their forehead one hour before washing. It is believed to make them more beautiful.

As a house plant, the aloe needs only a little water and the larger the pot the more rapidly it grows and produces off-shoots which, after a while, can be cut from the parent head and placed in their own pots. In this way, aloes will always be to hand.

Our Creator produces only harmony. We humans distort it and so produce disharmony. On obtaining understanding, we can restore harmony after our self-created grief and pain.

The split personality retains one half of the unit in the consciousness and represses the other half in the subconscious part of the soul. Subconsciously, we already have the answer and the solution to every question and every problem posed by the conscious mind.

Every illness resulting from one-sided living in the one half is accompanied by its cure in nature. Even for each *new* disease created by humans, nature immediately provides the cure! Those who are able to see this can help themselves and others.

13. Milk-Juice

Plants of Incarnation and Excarnation

The story that wild plants tell us never ceases to be an exciting one. So, too, is the history of our daily vegetables which have been developed from wild plants. Let us take a look at our garden lettuce and its ancestor, the wild or prickly lettuce, not forgetting the wild succory with its descendants the endive and chicory; and also the celandine, dandelion and sow-thistle, so plentiful in our gardens. Then there are the long-headed, corn and opium poppies, all related to our giant garden poppy.

These are all plants with milk-juice, generally white but a beautiful orange in the celandine. It generally tastes bitter and sometimes tart. In Venezuela, we find the 'cow's milk tree' which produces a white milk-juice that tastes just like cow's milk! Like everything with a bitter taste, this milk-juice contains the force of materialisation, of incarnation and strengthening, the force of the life ether and of the planets Mars and Saturn. Everything that tastes bitter and tart binds soul and body together, and keeps human or animal on earth. A bitter herb (wormwood) pulls a person back to life from the edge of the grave. It is a tonic for heart and liver. The milk-juice of plants is, of course, related to mother's milk in human and animal; they both help young created things to obtain material form and grow.

Our earthly globe itself was also once a young creation, with a weak body. This was in the Lemurian period, when the moon had not yet been born from the Earth. The Earth then hung like a cosmic embryo in the amniotic fluid, a yolk in the liquid egg-white, with its similar albuminous atmosphere from which all its creatures took nourishment. (They lived the way the starfish, for example, still does: this absorbs sea water and allows it to run through itself like blood and again excretes what it does not require.) This heavenly drink was called the holy *haoma* in ancient Persia and *soma* in India.

After the moon had escaped from the Earth in the area of the former Lemuria, now the Pacific Ocean, and the mistress of the waters had thus removed herself from the Earth, the latter began to dry up; water and land divided themselves from each other, and wrinkles (mountain chains) occurred. The atmosphere became thinner, the creatures strengthened their bodies and now absorbed the albuminous heavenly milk into their own systems which, originally spread out, now bent round about it; in this way the outside (ectoderm) and the inside (endoderm) of the body came about. In the plants, the heavenly milk became juice and with certain kinds of animal and human it changed into red blood.

In this red colouring matter lives the martial ego, the astral and coveted ego that plants do not as yet possess. Plants with milk-juice have retained this for some 50,000 years; these are ancient plants. The opium poppy and the spurge belong among them. The spurge (*euphorbia*) varieties are poisonous but from them good medicines can be made that calm spasms, expel water and mucus and parasites, abort, purge and widen the arteries. For this, the dried milk-juice is used. The seed of *euphorbia lathyris*, the caper spurge, can be roasted for a coffee-type drink.

The Opium Poppy

The opium poppy (*Papaver somniferum*) returns people to their lemuric state in a deep sleep full of dreams in which the pain and hurt of present-day earthly life disappear. Opium and its derivatives, morphine, codeine, etc., are, of course, made from the milk-juice of the unripe seed box. Opium stills the desperation with which the weak attempt to master their earthly life. Instead of strengthening them for this, it draws them away from their task, back to an earlier stage, back to the breast, even into the womb. And so it only lengthens their suffering along the great genetic journey through many earthly lives, because incarnation in matter and becoming the master of such matter is something we all have to learn.

Anyone who has arrived on Earth must obviously fulfil a task here. The flight to Lemuria only offers postponement. Apart from this, is it not remarkable how seas of corn poppies (*papaver rhoeas*) bloom in the battlefields? The pain-stillers appear where they are required!

The opium poppy is sometimes called the 'moon poppy' and a variety of this is the blue poppy, whole fields of which, are cultivated, for example on the islands of southern Holland, with fine dark-purple flowers. Its black seed is the poppy seed baked on to Greek bread and these can also be pressed to provide oil for margarine. Its relationship with lunar force is clear from its name. Opium and the like does in fact return humans to the moon, the Earth's nearest neighbour, where the souls of the unborn reside together with the souls who have just died.

When our task on Earth is done, we arrive there by ourselves. If you have poppies in your garden, just watch how arrival on Earth and departure from Earth are expressed in this plant. When the flower buds develop, they first hang heavily towards the ground since, as with all hanging flowers — campanulas, bleeding hearts, laburnum, wisteria and suchlike — the earth is still pulling at them (life-ether, Saturn). On opening itself up, the flower turns to the sun and becomes a mass of fire. The saturnine can still be seen in the black spots at the foot of the petals and the black pollen. After that, the seed box ripens upright like a candle, drawn towards the moon. In this way it passes through three stages: earth (ascetic), sun and moon.

Garden Lettuce

Our garden lettuce (*Lactuca sativa*), as the Latin name indicates, is a juicy milk-plant (French: *laitue*), dripping with milk-juice when the root is cut off fresh. Amongst other things, it contains bromide and its effect is therefore calming and soothing. For this reason, the Romans ate it in the evening, as a sleeping potion at the end of a meal.

In the Middle Ages, wild lettuce was used to prepare the narcotic Lactucarium Germanicum which was much more bitter than Lactucarium Gallicum produced from garden lettuce. The wild or prickly lettuce (*Lactuca virosa*) has small leaves but continues to be cultivated in increasingly more tender form. In fact, the leafy bud was arrested and enlarged, so that the head is really a baby! The Persian kings were already eating it in 500 BC and amongst the ancient Hebrews it was one of the bitter herbs of Seder before Easter, together with chicory and endive. The juice of the wild lettuce cannot be taken raw but a homoeopathic medicine is made of it: Lactuca Virosa D3 (5 drops three times daily) against asthma, cramp and insomnia. If the garden lettuce is allowed to bolt and produce a flower, its original shape will be recognised, with a head of small yellow flowers.

Sow-Thistle

The sow-thistle (*Sonchus oleraceus*), sown in our gardens by Mother Nature, provides a good salad, particularly when mixed with garden lettuce. (After all, oleraceus means 'edible as a vegetable'.) Its names point to the animals that value it: the sow, the goose ('goose-thistle' in German) and the hare ('hare-thistle' in French). The effect of the leaves is refrigerant, stimulating the gall bladder and alterative. They cure hepatitis, jaundice, stone, asthma, enteritis, pleurisy and painful urination. They form milk and purify the blood. Anyone who cannot obtain the fresh leaf should take tea from dried leaves. Sedative plants like the garden lettuce and sow-thistle are like the soothing hands of a mother — just as a moon plant should be.

14. Potato

The potato (*Solanum tuberosum*) belongs to the poisonous plant family of the *Solanaceae* which, in its mother country, America, has provided so many of the poisons used by the native peoples. These included tobacco and the thorn-apple (*Datura stramonium*) which was used to loosen the ethereal body from the material body, to enable people to meet their ancestors (to become 'high' as it is called nowadays). The tomato, too, is not entirely innocent, and then, in Europe, we find other members of the family — henbane (a component of witch-salve), deadly nightshade (*Atropa belladonna*), bittersweet and black nightshade. The potato, an underground tuber, is also a poisonous plant but its poison, solanine, is contained only in the leaf, flower and fruit, and in the eyes of the potato. Poison is also produced in those parts of the potato which have lain in the light and have become green. If you eat potatoes in the jacket, you must always clean them well and cut away any green parts.

However, this tuber is otherwise a relatively good food, and although it consists of 90 per cent water, making the eater put on weight, its remaining 10 per cent contains potassium (1 kg of potatoes produces 5g of potassium and potassium produces muscles — just look at Van Gogh's potato-eating peat-cutters!). And, immediately beneath the peel, there is a little silicic acid which is lost when they are peeled. If potatoes are boiled in their jackets in water, the potassium and silicic acid will pass into the water and therefore it must not be thrown away but made into soup or used as a purgative taken on an empty stomach: carrots, celeriac and linseed must then be boiled with it. Further, the potato is also a rich source of vitamin C, which gives protection against infection.

Remedial Value

The potato cures glycosuria (glucose in the urine) and abnormal thirst (polydipsia) and increases vitality in the tissues. For inflammation of the kidneys, a poultice of potatoes boiled in their jackets without salt to a puree is placed, while still warm, on the patient's back above the kidneys, with a cloth over it. After six hours at the most, it should be removed and buried, because the toxin of the sickness has been attracted into the puree. Then place a fresh poultice and continue until the patient has recovered. A wart can be rubbed with a fresh potato peel. Slices of raw potato can be worn in thin bags on painful places for lumbago, sciatica, swollen knees and painful arms, legs and feet. Replace them with fresh ones as soon as they have dried. Packs of grated raw potato can be placed on burns and other wounds.

Freshly pressed potato juice is drunk against excessive stomach acid. This can also be given to young babies when milk is insufficient. Potato juice, drunk freshly pressed in the morning and at night, taken from a pound of potatoes in each case, is a cure that can be successfully applied for the disease that has now become so common, spondylosis — deterioration of the discs between the vertebrae. Make your back healthy, straight, supple and strong again, without a corset or operation!

A pap of boiled potatoes and fresh buttermilk can be placed three times a day in a circle round swellings and painful places indicating an internal inflammation, possibly of a tubercular nature — and on swollen legs.

Water in which potatoes have been boiled will make paintings, copper, silver and your own hands as clean as a new pin and thins fruit stains in linen, after which they disappear in the wash. So, admire the potato and use it.

15. Thistle

Thistles are amongst the herbs that bring many benefits to humankind but which, in some countries, are being systematically eradicated. In Belgium, for example, it is a criminal act not to destroy wild thistles on your land. Many varieties are both a food and a medicine for human and animal.

Examine the structure of the plant. You will see that the thistle is dry by nature and seeks the sunlight more than water. The leaves become steadily drier, harder and more spiney towards the edges. The sepals, too, which surround the flowerhead, project sharply. However, the flower itself, generally purple but sometimes yellow, consists of soft tubular florets that often smell sweet. They radiate sun force.

So we see Mars at work in the spines, the sun in the flower and Jupiter in the substances that the thistle contains, as feeder and healer, especially for his own organ, the liver. Bitter substances and the nutritive carbohydrate inulin occur in most kinds. The former, in particular, strengthen the ego, which then has its effect on the digestion, granting protection against poison through the liver and promoting Mars-related production of gall. People who need to defend themselves better, who must become more self-sufficient, will benefit from eating such thistles as the cardoon and artichoke or from the medicine, for example milk-thistle seed.

Artichoke (Cynara scolymus)

The artichoke is a large thistle with fine purple flowers commonly cultivated as a vegetable in southern Europe. The base of the flower and the lower ends of the sepals are eaten. The heads are cut into four pieces, the stamens removed, the pieces are washed under a jet of water and are braised in oil, till tender, together with a bay leaf and a few cloves. As soon as a sepal comes away easily during cooking the dish in ready. This is an excellent food for liver and nerves.

Dr Vogel has processed artichoke into his medicine 'Boldo-cynara' and the anthroposophists (Messrs. Holle) prepare an artichoke syrup from it. The leaf and root contain bitters, tannin, provitamin A and a little vitamin B_1. Also present is the enzyme cynarase which works actively as a rennet (and so separates milk) and which is used in the south in cheesemaking, greatly improving the human digestion of milk-albumen.

Welted or Scottish Thistle (Onopordon acanthium)

The chief food of donkeys, when they can find them, is thistles, especially the welted thistle, which they seem to prefer. This gives them the strength and stamina to make long journeys, laden with heavy burdens, along steep mountain tracks in heat or cold. The thistles are tonics, stimulating the glandular system. The donkey comes under the sign Cancer which, in the East, is also called the Donkey. It is believed that Jesus was born in Gemini, between Taurus and Cancer, i.e. between the bull and donkey. It is a friendly, willing sign, which takes up the burdens of others but can be rather obstinate in behaviour. The crab or donkey is governed by the moon, which controls the glands in humans and animals.

Used as a medicine for people, the plant is a diuretic, stomachic and febrifuge; the root also promotes menstruation.

Blessed Thistle (Cnicus benedictus or Carduus benedictus)

This type of thistle is to be found throughout Europe, but chiefly in the Balkans. It has yellow flowers. The ancient Romans used it to reinforce the heart and liver. Charlemagne followed them in this. Martin Luther took *Kardobenediktenwasser* against the pains in his left thigh: swelling of the spleen. According to the doctrine of signatures, these spiny plants are particularly good against shooting pains.

The blessed thistle (*Chardon beni* in French, *Benediktenkraut* in German) improves the function of the liver and is therefore also a specific against pernicious anaemia, swollen liver, gall-stones, jaundice and obstruction of the portal vein. It stimulates transpiration, menstruation, the stomach glands and the kidneys and eliminates fever and worms.

16. The Borage Family

The borage family of plants (*Asperifoliaceae* or *Boraginaceae*) is distinguished by its hairy leaves, its flowers coloured pink to blue and its close affinity with silicic acid. This substance, silicea, is associated with light but can also absorb large quantities of water. We therefore find borages like the common comfrey on damp ground, along the edges of ditches and on riverbanks. In its rough hairs we recognise silicic acid which always creates sharp, pointed forms (Sagittarius). Silicic acid provides hexagonal crystals found in the rock crystal which are also sharp and pointed. To people who take these plants to heart it grants sturdiness and single-mindedness. Its flowers takes the form of a spiral that gradually unrolls: the bud unfolds in the light. These flowers contain plenty of nectar, deep inside, which the bees must unroll their tongues to obtain.

These plants do full justice to both yang and yin in their colouring, from red (yang, acid) to blue (yin, alkaline) and vice versa; the roots, too, sometimes furnish a red dye (henna red). This is analogous with the balance between light and water. This property gives them curative powers in human ailments where this balance is upset. For example, with a ganglion (enlarged swelling), arising through a heavy blow on the bone near a joint, the fluid is pressed from the joint and ossifies into an additional layer on the bone. This can be a great nuisance, for instance on the tail-bone. The leaf and preparation from the comfrey can in the long run cause this hardness to dissolve into a fluid.

Forget-me-not

The humble charming blue flower of the forget-me-not (*Myosotis*) in its various varieties and its downy leaves shows preference for the yin side. It is a symbol of that far-off ideal which people (Sagittarius) seek to the end of the earth. It appeals to the emotions.

It is a comforting and curing little plant for soul and body alike. It is used against chronic bronchitis, TB of the lungs, intestinal bleeding and night sweats. It gives strength to those who have lost their taste for life on earth.

Common Gromwell

The Latin name of the gromwell (*Lithospermum officinale*) has a double meaning: silicic acid in chalk makes the seeds of this plant as hard as stone but it also — remember the symbolism — cures people of gallstone. Furthermore, it is a contraceptive and can prevent pregnancy.

Lungwort

Another member of the family is the lungwort (*Pulmonaria officinalis*) which with its spotted heart-shaped leaves and pink to blue coloured flowers is a pleasing garden plant which continues to seed itself. Its rough, hairy leaves can be rubbed on the chest for ailments of the bronchial passages and a tea can be made from them for the same purpose.

In spring the young leaves can be eaten in salads, their effect being slightly astringent (good for diarrhoea, for example) and they are popular in Britain as a spring green. The tea has a mild calming and expectorant effect on the bronchial passages. In the past, powdered lungwort was also used in the French medicament Pulmo, though this is no longer the case, and this powder, sprinkled on fresh wounds, promotes healing. Mixed with honey, it can be administered for blood disease and diarrhoea. Recipes for a tea for congested lungs and the like:

1. Take one part of violet leaf and one part of liquorice to three parts of lungwort, plantain (preferably the ribwort variety) and colt's foot.

2. Equal parts of lungwort, plantain and common fennel.

Of each of these teas, add 15 g (1/2 oz) of mixture to half a litre of boiling water. Take a dessertspoonful every two hours.

Tea against weak bladder, piles, blood in the urine and a tendency to gravel and stone: lungwort, speedwell and chervil, all fresh. Three cupsful a day.

Comfrey

Comfrey (*Symphytum officinalis*) has now become very popular again. The cosmic force which gives plants their wound-healing effect is the astringent force of Saturn. It can be recognised by the outer appearance of the plant — so comfrey and marigold have leaves which partly do not grow on stems but appear direct from the stalk or even remain attached to it for some length, as if they just cannot bear to let go. The comfrey is saturnine through and through: the flowers hang downwards in a row of purple or whitish yellow bells, each with five lappets, i.e. each consisting of five flower petals. These bells open downwards, thus looking at the earth and therefore associated with closed, introverted people, with the Capricorn type, an earth sign, which cleaves so strongly to convention.

In the past, comfrey was abundant along the edges of ditches and low banks. The leaves are very hairy and the flowers contain a great deal of nectar and are frequently visited by bees. The fatty root, containing white milk-juice, is covered with a black skin just like the scorzonera and is just as edible. This root (*Radix symphyti* to the herbalists) is particularly medicinal, especially for healing fractures (Greek: *symphein* = coalesce). The Latin name is *Consolida*, the German *Beinwell* and the French *grande consoude*, an alternative English name being 'knitbone'.

An ointment (salve) can be prepared from it and Dr Vogel uses the root in his 'Creme Symphytum' (though this is the Siberian comfrey). The fresh root can be grated and beaten to a paste with hot water. A little prepared loam (e.g., Luvos Heilerde) is rubbed on a cloth, the paste placed on it and the whole positioned on the fracture. Three spoonsful of root ground to a powder can also be prepared with boiling water.

The comfrey will rapidly cure fractures of the bone but the paste or the symphytum extract can also be applied to phlegmona (acute inflammation of the cell tissues, with suppuration), festering sores, carbuncles, blocked varicose veins, piles, gangrene, whitlow, rheumatic and arthritic inflammations, pain in the bones, septic bone, swollen joints, softening and inflammation of the bone, nerve pains and damage, and to the stump of an amputation, sprains and strains, sciatica, swellings, open sores, etc. The narcotic effect of the root will be evident if it is chewed.

Symphytum (i.e., the original tincture) can be taken internally in water or in tea of the ground root (15 drops to a cup) for stroke, bleeding, chronic peritonitis, stomach and duodenal ulcer, chronic catarrh of the bronchial passages, excessive menstruation and bloody urine or diarrhoea. Three teaspoonsful of the tincture are taken and continued, when the bleeding has stopped, with 20 drops in water or tea three times a day.

Care must be taken when using the leaves. Placed fresh on wounds their effect is curative, promoting the growth of new tissues. Like the leaves of the common borage, their effect is cleansing and curative when placed on cancerous swellings (the fetid air disappears, as does the pain). These leaves of the comfrey, which grows wild in this country, contain a substance, however, which is toxic to the nervous system. Cattle do not eat it. However, there are other varieties which are in fact grown as animal fodder, particularly for pigs. These are the *Symphytum asperinum* in the Caucasus, the *S. peregrinum* in the Ukraine and the *S. orientale* in Armenia and northern Prussia. Then there is also the *S. siberica* which Dr Vogel uses in his cream.

These cultivated varieties contain vitamin B_{12} (just like Iceland moss). In the English-speaking world, these varieties are cultivated for comfrey salad made from the leaves. The juices in the leaf and, even more so, in the root, by promoting the creation of new skin tissue, can cause wrinkles and folds in the skin to disappear and are therefore useful in cosmetics. If you want to gather the roots, you should do so in the early spring or autumn as the substances they contain are then at their most effective. In the case of an accident, 20 drops are given in water or a comfrey tea made from a mixture of four tinctures which together repair everything that may be damaged: muscles, nerves, veins, bones and also the affective soul — Symphytum O, Arnica D2, Hypericum D1 and Calendula O, in equal parts (O means 'original tincture', i.e. undiluted).

Borage

One of the plants that do well in a cold summer is the borage (*Borage officinalis*) with its bunches of sky-blue star-shaped flowers. It is often sown as a honey bee plant. The stalks, leaves and flowers can be eaten. Gather the fallen flowers every day and use them to decorate a salad.

The nitrate of potassium this plant contains combats inflammations. In particular, this herb stimulates the effect of the cortical

area of the adrenal glands — read this carefully if you are sometimes treated with cortisone. Borage therefore helps you make your
own cortisone. It relieves you of deposits of uric acid (acidose, acid-
ification) which produce rheumatics, and cures inflammation of
the kidneys and bladder.

It also strengthens the nerves, the leaves being chopped up in
salad to calm nervous people. It soothes irritations, lifts you up out
of your depressions, sends peaceful sleep, cools fevers, strengthens the heart and carries off poisons in increased urine. In short, it
relieves you of much evil.

A leaf can be pressed out together with the mixed vegetables
of which you drink a glass of juice a day. A tea can also be infused
from it (8 g or $1/3$ oz of flowers or 20 g or $3/4$ oz of leaves to half a
litre of boiling water). The flowers are, moreover, a decorative addition to your garden.

17. The Bramble

At the back of my garden there are wild brambles just like those
to be found at the edges of woods and on the heath and in the
dunes. Now the leaves are brown and the hard edges of their long,
low shoots waving in the wind rub over each other. When brambles rustle in the wind, the Germans say, the winter will be a sharp
one. When walking past them, take care that their sharp, slightly
bent, downward-pointing thorns do not hook into your clothes or
tear your hand open. A bramble hedge is the best protection for a
place that you want to keep inaccessible. For that reason, sacred
places were surrounded with them of old. A common place name
in Germany is Maria im Dornhag, (Mary in the Thornhedge), an
ancient holy spot where, later, a statue of the Virgin was placed.

However, the thorns serve not only as a weapon; they guide the
fire force (see their red hue) which carries with it the life spirit as
it descends on earth. The brambles surround their prince like fiery
knights and pass on their strength. The burning bramble! Where
brambles grow, there is a power point.

The human aspect may be seen in its flowers of five (like the
wild rose, the apple and other members of the family). Five is the

figure of humanity. The five-pointed star that points upwards is the sign of the human striving onward, who makes a pentangle when standing with arms outspread and legs apart. In ancient initiation caves a pentangle will be found cut into the rock wall, in which the initiate had to stand. We also have twice five toes and twice five fingers, with which we grip earth and space. Five is the number of the will. (Remember, also, the five-fold top flower of the rue.)

The bramble leaf is sometimes three-, sometimes five- and sometimes seven-part. A five-part leaf is like a hand: the force of human over matter. Every summer, the bramble produces long new shoots which literally reach round itself. If a young shoot finds a high vantage point in hedge or tree, it grows upwards but if it touches the earth, then it develops roots at that spot which penetrate the soil and so cause a new plant to appear. In this way, the bramble corresponds with humans, who are active in both spiritual and earthly life, industrious and fruitful people, adapting to circumstances, coping with whatever comes along.

From the young shoots, a tea may be made against inflammation of the skin. The fresh shoots, leaves and flowers may be infused with boiling water into a good rinse and gargle for sore throats and mouth ailments, inflamed tonsils, swollen gums and stomatitis. The fire force kills harmful germs and the tannin tones the mucous membranes and gums (Mars and Saturn). The tannic acid links the pole of thought and the pole of life of more or less split personalities and reunites them into one piece.

It strengthens the nerves, particularly those of the digestion and dries excessive water (lymphatic, vegetative, moon-type), so bramble leaf tea is also effective against diarrhoea, leucorrhoea and moist cough. Drunk in the last month of pregnancy, bramble tea strengthens the muscles which will shortly have to expel the child and will thereby ease and speed up labour. The fresh bramble leaf may be placed with its white underside on inflammations of the skin to draw out the evil. The root of the bramble may, chopped finely, be boiled for twenty minutes and the water then drunk with honey against dropsy.

The fruits — the blackberries — are rich in vitamins and minerals and a tasty food. The juice strengthens the walls of the arteries.

The forces of the bramble can therefore be taken up by humans in order to strengthen themselves and others. But also listen to its rustling story of old times that will return, of bramble hedges round holy places of power. It is broadcast for anyone who wishes to hear. Even now. So that people may become aware in fiery prayer and fiery deed — I am the flame of God! Walk across the field and listen.

18. Stagshorn Clubmoss

(Family: *Lycopodiaceae*)

The stagshorn clubmoss is a very ancient plant. At the beginning of plant life on earth the clubmosses grew to an enormous height. Now, they are to be found only, and rarely at that, on lonely heaths. The stalk with its fine leaves creeps, the side branches turn upwards and sometimes carry two yellow ears with spore-boxes, containing the spores, a yellow powder. This powder contains aluminium. If a match is put to it, it explodes. The ripe spores end up in the ground and after some seven years a preliminary form develops from this with male and female organs, after which the asexual plant itself arises.

Active in this plant are, first of all, Pluto, then Saturn and Neptune. It belongs to the beginning and the end of earth life and human life. It is therefore used chiefly for children and old people.

The spore powder is used by the chemist to roll pills in, to keep them dry. In that state it is inactive. Only by prolonged rubbing are the envelopes of the spores broken so that the active component, called pollenin, is released. It is given in D12 and higher. It quickly deteriorates.

Corresponding Human Type

The human type associated with Lycopodium is the saturnine, lean, perspicuous and hair-splitting-sagacious type, with weak muscles. Intelligence has developed to a high pitch, at the expense of the body, which is weakly. Such a child is often old beyond his or her years, with a well developed head on a weak body. People of this type prefer mental work, often sit silently and suffer from uric acid. They are very irritable; first of all they complain that no one is interested in them, yet if someone does come along, they are snubbed and are made unwelcome.

It is typical of such persons that they are always set on matching their forces with the people roundabout them; physically the weaker, they try to obtain the upper hand mentally — the power aspects of Pluto and the authority aspects of Saturn. In childhood and old age they quickly become the underdog. For someone over the age of 70 whose ego emanates too weakly and is therefore bullied by carers, the roles can be reversed by a few grains of Lycopodium D30 or 200 once a month.

The Power of Stagshorn Clubmoss

Lycopodium in fact has a strong influence on the stream of forces that begin at the anus and flow upwards to the brain. This force stream strengthens the ego. If the flow becomes too weak, so that the ego can no longer defend itself against stronger egos, we then prefer not to be confronted with those other egos! As a result, the tension placed on the anus in order to push this force upwards is sometimes too great. Through this stress bowel motions are impeded even though the desire is there — a typical phenomenon.

Amongst old people, the flow is often no longer sufficient for the brain and they become forgetful; they are no longer able to find the right words and confuse facts. In this case, phosphorus helps but Lycopodium does so in a wider area. In this type, the liver function is weak and this often produces local swelling and noises, particularly lower in the stomach, through inadequate digestion. Frequently, this runs parallel with annoyance about subordinates or pupils. It is all interlinked. We notice that a patient of this kind comes to the table hungry but is suddenly replete after a few mouthfuls — a typical phenomenon of Lycopodium. New layers of skin continually appear in the nose.

The right-hand side of the body is linked to the mind and is therefore the more active with this type of person; it is here that all processes start. Pain, for example, travels from right to left. The right foot becomes cold when the left is still warm.

Lycopodium also helps with fractures on the right-hand side.

Another typical phenomenon of Lycopodium is reddish urine with a sand-like sediment. Before this occurs, pain is sometimes felt in the kidneys, i.e. in the back. The red sand can be a harbinger of kidney gravel and stone.

Finally, Lycopodium is also suitable for certain kinds of bronchitis and pneumonia, namely those which are chiefly attributable to a combination of mental work, sitting still and bad air or the waste fumes from a gas stove or car exhaust. It begins with a dry cold and a blocked nose, then the air passages fill with a thick yellow or green mucus, the patient feels constricted and his nostrils move up and down like fans in order to obtain more air. Typical in this case is that the mucus tastes salty or bitter and that the patient feels his worst between 4 and 8 pm. The skin becomes grey with yellowish or brown patches and there is a feeling of tiredness and listlessness and a great need for fresh air.

Lycopodium is an excellent remedy against psoriasis, a Saturnian ailment, and is the specific for intellectuals who lack vitality.

19. The Goose-Foot Family

The Rune

The goose-foot as a rune is the lower half of the tree of life: the trunk with the three roots that embrace the underworld. The centre root is portrayed as somewhat longer and when its end is then linked to the other two roots we have more or less the shape of the leaf that certain plants of the goose-foot family possess. It is also the shape of the three-toed foot of the goose. The Peace movement uses this rune as its symbol.

This rune is the emblem of winter, death and the underworld, of the root, thought and abstraction; in brief, of Saturn. It belongs to the Germanic goddess Berchta, who receives the souls of the departed and who governs in the winter months. She is a mythical figure who in later times was confused with the historical Bertha of the Great Foot, the mother of Charlemagne. This two-sided figure has lived on in folk memory as Mother Goose.

And now, these plants are indeed a product in which the forces of Saturn and the moon, the poles of thought and of life, root and leaf, act together in a specific combination. It might be said that this plant family represents the Saturn-moon axis. Essentially in opposition: shrinkage and expansion, dry and wet, death and life, abstraction and concentration, together they keep living creatures in balance. The root can fetch up the minerals from the soil with the aid of the water in which they are dissolved and the sugar made by the juicy leaves is stored in the root, for example in the beetroot and sugar-beet. In this way, the saturnine root and the moon leaf collaborate.

Salt Plants

The goose-foots (*Chenopodiaceae*) include the salt plants, i.e. the edible glasswort, the cultivated orach, spinach, beetroot, sugar-beet and the mangel-wurzel (cattle fodder), beet spinach and swede. It is, therefore, a very nutritious family. They possess a wealth of mineral salts, and common salt. After all, in the blueprint of human and of plant we can, like Paracelsus, distinguish two poles and their connection.

Sulphur, Salt and Mercury

Sulphur, one of the original substances from which life was derived (the egg yolk) belongs to the moon, the pole of life, the flower of the plant and the sexual organs in humans; it is the pole of Incarnation. It conveys the creative force of the sun into matter: sul-phur = sol-fer = sun-bearer.

Common salt is the concentration of forces belonging to Saturn and the pole of thought, to the root of the plant and the human head. Mercury, or quicksilver, aids circulation between the two poles. It belongs to Mercury, to the stalk and leaves, to the flow of the juices. The salt plants (halophytes) in this family are such salt-lovers that they grow by preference along the sea coast. They include the glasswort (*Salicornia*) and the saltwort (*Salsola*) which both contain a lot of soda (soda is obtained from their ashes) and are rich in potassium salts. They also like growing close to people. The saltwort and glasswort have the fleshiness of leaves that have to contain much water in order to retain the salts in them (after standing the glasswort in fresh water for a while it can be cooked and eaten). Here, we can clearly see the moon (water) collaborating with Saturn (salts).

Beetroot

The beetroot displays a root (pole of thought) that has linked itself closely to the forces that really belong to the pole of life, the flower: the red colour and the sugar. It is swollen with it, dropsy-like.

This indicates that the plant is a good medicine for illnesses where balance between the poles has been disturbed and the fresh juice of beetroot is an excellent curative both for cancer (excess of the pole of life) and for multiple sclerosis (excess of the pole of thought). The MS patient is dried up through too little moon love (dependence, pampering, cuddling, comfort); if they are given beetroot juice, their strong Saturn will attach to the root but water and sugar (pole of life) are also supplied.

The cancer patient, conversely, has a teeming pole of life owing to the absence of any overflow channel outwards; the moon in them will attach directly to the water and sugar, but the root force is also supplied. This helps them to become conscious of their surplus of feeling and to abstract it into wisdom.

Beetroot also contains a great deal of saponin and pectin and the radioactive substance ribidium helps those kinds of cancer that are commonly caused by radioactive fall-out from nuclear explosions, such as leukaemia and cancer of the bone). These three substances promote digestion and are good for the bladder and skin.

Worming Agents

The beetroot and the orange carrot (the same combination of poles, orange and sweet belong to the flower and fruit, to the pole of life), when eaten raw, are a good substance against the larvae that so often occur in small children at the moon age (0 to 7 years) (beetroot, carrots and onion only, on an empty stomach at full moon) and the leaf and seed of the North African goose-foot (*Chenopodium anthelminticum*) produce an oil used against intestinal worms.

Intestinal parasites can live and multiply only in an environment with an excess of moon force, i.e. proportionately too little Saturn. But supplying pure saturnine products would not help as they are not assimilated. The access to the medicament is the moon component in the red or orange root, the pole of life aspect. The saturnine accompanies it, inhibits the reproduction and paralyses the parasites. You can now see why larvae are found most commonly amongst children less given to thinking and still progressing in the pole of life, and why people say that larvae (and lice) are the products of an 'excess of health'.

Spinach

Beet spinach, turnip (the Swiss variety) and orach make fine vegetables, as do the foliage and stems of the beetroot. They are chopped and cooked in a little oil and chopped onion. Spinach is better known, and is widely praised for its richness in iron, but is still not always a healthy vegetable.

As a rule, it is heavily cultivated with artificial nitrogen fertiliser so that it becomes poisonous. Many people become ill from it in the spring. Further, spinach contains large quantities of oxalic acid, like the rhubarb, sorrel and tomato. This can be neutralised by adding egg. This is why we eat spinach with eggs and rhubarb with a beaten egg.

Oxalic acid breaks up blockages in the flow of juices, helps incarnation, and strengthens the moon. (Some small children will eat wood sorrel straight from the open field.) It may be regarded as a vegetable forerunner of formic acid in the animal kingdom as produced by ants and bees and which is a great neutraliser of uric acid. People who are very ego-conscious through a strong Saturn produce much uric acid from the albumen in their food and this supports their ego-consciousness. Their pole of thought is commonly strengthened at the expense of their pole of life, of their moon and Mars. This leads eventually to people with a clear, active mental apparatus and a rigid body, poisoned through an excess of uric acid. Patients of this kind need oxalic acid and formic acid in order to stimulate their pole of life and should eat honey. The busy ants and bees have a strong Mars.

A wasp, lazy (pole of life), has an alkaline sting, so place acid on it (vinegar, lemon juice). A bee, industrious (pole of thought), has formic acid in its sting, so put alkali on it (ammonia). Apis (bee) is given for the right-hand ovary, vespa (wasp) for the left-hand one.

The root of spinach (rich in saponin and iron) with sassafras is an anthroposophic medicine against pernicious anaemia (where

Mars consumes too much leaf colourant for the preparation of gall colourant).

20. Rose and Lily

Five is the figure of humankind. With arms and legs outspread, the human body fits into a regular pentagon. We have twice five fingers and twice five toes. In this, our essence expresses itself. Draw a regular pentagon with a five-pointed star in it, and allow this design to impress itself on you.

Consider the five 72° angles, the quintiles, around the centre. Compare the five-pointed star with the six-pointed (six sextiles). The six-pointed one is at static rest (Venus) and the five-pointed one in dynamic movement (Mercury). In the latter, consciousness originates! This will already be clear if five points are drawn as they appear on dice: four in a square, with one in its centre. These four, the four elements, form the waiting material. Something happens to it when the spirit, as the fifth factor, the quintessential, descends in their midst, like the consciousness of matter.

Now, something emerges from this substance apart from its own shape and knows or is conscious of what this is. Five is the number of the wild rose. Six the number of the lily. The rose belongs with humans, while the lily is unearthly, heavenly, cosmic. (The lily, portrayed next to the Virgin when the Angel Gabriel visits her, indicates that Mary's soul was turned towards heaven.) The lily makes few roots, feeding itself from its bulb, its own cosmos. It flowers on earth like a gift from heaven but without associating with the earth; it knows nothing of good and evil. It signifies purity.

The rose, on the other hand, spreads just enough roots to achieve balance between heaven and earth. It is the sign of harmony — a representation of the spiritual fire of the sun in the human heart. It is the sign of love. The rose stands central in the full of life. It spreads its branches with its five (sometimes seven) leaves roundabout. It smells and pricks: it certainly gives itself but must also defend itself in order to maintain its place in the struggle of life. It offers both love and pain. And it hides a great secret in itself (sub rosa), the secret of human happiness that lies in balance achieved through the sacred marriage of the poles.

The rose belongs to those who are prepared to suffer for their happiness, who embrace life in its fullness, here and now. Those who live on earth with the knowledge of God in their hearts.

Five and Will Power

Five is the number of the human will. Five-leaved flowers strengthen the will so that it gathers the forces of the soul and the four elements round it in obedience, like the prince does the knights of his court. Think of the topmost, five-leaf flower of the rue, governing the four-leaved, the will reaffirmed above the passions, so we do not become drunk from the wine!

All the *rosaceae* with five flowers therefore have something of the effect of gathering together, inducing self control: the bramble and apple, the silverweed, the tormentil and lady's mantle, and the creeping cinquefoil.

Five is the figure of those who are in control of themselves and their lives. The royal person. Five combined into one and one radiating outwards as five is the Sun — the centre of the glyph of Mercury, the spiritual spark in the heart, the scale of the moon above it and the cross of matter beneath it: the spirit between soul and body, holding ether and substance together. With each breath, the sun force penetrating into us gathers ether and substance together, so that our ethereal or life body is stretched tightly over our material body. And once we draw our last breath, we return the spirit and then ether and substance let go of each other entirely.

Five is the figure of the human as magician (Tarot), of the force and strength of humankind as long as it expresses God's spirit in human life.

Five is the number of humans as creators, as artists who have to struggle — to guide fire through matter, so that they leave their mark in it behind them.

Five is the number of the life struggle — whoever endures to the last will be crowned with roses.

21. The Scrophulariaceae

Herbs of the Pain of Love and Estrangement

As in animals, specific human types can also be distinguished in plants. Or specific human properties, problems or ailments. Generally, a plant is also then the medicine for that complaint. Take, for example, the family of snapdragons (*Scrophulariaceae*), which include the toadflax and the garden antirrhinums, the small foxglove, the figwort, the bird's eye speedwell and brooklime, eyebright, mullein and greater foxglove. Of these, the large foxglove is poisonous, but good medicine is made from it.

Various herbs in this family are used against jaundice, piles, eczema, and heart and kidney disease. This brings us immediately to the subject of bottled-up feelings, frustration, disappointment in love and deep distress.

Jaundice is linked with vexation, with Mars force which is not allowed out (we may not be insolent to our parents or the boss and so brood in silence) and this force then turns inwards, back into the body.

Piles are swellings of the veins, like varicose veins in the legs; and, in parallel, the ego holds fast onto sorrowful feelings, instead of placing them on God's altar, the heart. A Venus-Saturn affliction.

Eczema is, in many cases, also an expression of inability to process and communicate emotions. The force of Venus: the love that wishes to unfold and which for this is directed to another being but is not accepted then turns back to its own body as a poison.

If we can get over the disappointment, the kidneys will remove the poison. It is even better if the event can be processed and understood and so sublimated to human experience, self-knowledge and wisdom, the poison then being converted into creative force at a higher plane.

The Poison of Self-Love

When the saturnine ego (self-love) causes the disappointment to solidify into feelings of injustice and self-pity, and because the ego prefers to remain important as a victim, we retain the poison and it generally creeps into the skin. This is an organ of Venus insofar as it is the area that is caressed, while at the same time it is an organ of Saturn, delimiting and closing off the body. This is why Venus-Saturn conflicts are so frequently expressed through the skin. Psoriasis (silvery, fla! ing skin) for example, is an illness of people whose love has been rejected and who have been disappointed by their partner. And how does that happen? Often because love is offered in a way that does not suit the partner, and so finds no point of application in them; people in fact give what they themselves want to receive (too inclined towards Saturn) while the partner is quite different and so requires a different kind of love, and has to be approached quite differently. Such people offer gifts that do not please the other, because they have no need of them or they do not suit their taste, and then complain about ingratitude.

They must learn to recognise that the disappointment lies within themselves. The tragedy of psoriasis patients is that firstly they cannot be relieved of their love because of this too egocentric attitude (psychological ignorance) and secondly they are spurned as an erotic partner because of their off-putting skin. For them, this is the hard, bitter lesson that must lead to insight. Often, people of this kind are combined with a similar partner in order to learn the lesson from each other. For example, the one wishes to make love, the other to sublimate, and since they both continue to sulk they both become frustrated. A man who himself decided to take piano lessons urged his wife, in his short-sightedness, to do the same. She, who much preferred to busy herself with housekeeping, took revenge with the same short-sightedness by honouring him on his birthday with a new kind of floor cloth.

Heart and kidney complaints are the immediate result and symptom of distress that can be neither cast out nor processed and which then changes to a poison that affects the kidneys that have to excrete it.

Antirrhinum

Let us now take a closer look at the *Scrophulariceae*. The toadflax or garden antirrhinum have a flower consisting of two parts or lips that close on each other, just like the tightly pressed lips of an injured marriage partner. When an insect settles on the lower lip, it sags downwards through its weight, so that the animal can enter the doorway and fertilise the stamen. On its departure, the flower regains its closed, forbidding face, in just the same way as the 'love life' of such marriage partners proceeds. The toadflax has a long root stalk — it quickly runs elsewhere with all its troubles, 'to someone who understands it better'.

And why do we make tea from the toadflax (the herbalist's *Herba Linariae*? It acts against jaundice and weakness of the sphincter muscle of the anus (a common complaint amongst older people). It does, after all, close itself, holding fast to its troubles and the poisonous waste of its emotional life.

Figwort

The figwort (*Scrophularia nodosa*) has a different kind of angry face. The sharply outward-facing leaves stand crosswise to the sharp, square stalk: it is hard and obdurate and is aware that it is, and carries, a cross. Knobbly flowers appear at the upper end, brown at the top, yellow beneath, with a thick bunch of stamens between them. They smell nasty. The root stock is fat. It is just as if the plant is saying "You won't catch me submitting!"

An ointment against piles is made from the root stock. And tea can be infused from the herb, against all kinds of knobbliness (nodes — hence *nodosa*), against swollen glands (i.e. scrophula), and especially against an enlarged thyroid and eczema. Generally speaking, glands swell because they absorb poisons, poisons of bitter and hateful thoughts which we do not wish to release. The thyroid swells when we over-tire ourselves through not being entirely happy with the work we do, and holds back our egos. And also when we devote ourselves to sexual intercourse without being in love, without enjoying it, without giving ourselves up to it — then, there is no invigorating exchange, only exhaustion.

Foxglove

The foxglove (*Digitalis purpurea*) which provides us with the well-known heart remedy is again a closed Saturn plant which in the shade opens up, one by one, its purple glove-fingers with dotted honey markings; it presages calamity — and it is very *poisonous*. It is associated with cardiac asthma, with the square or conjunction of Sun and Saturn, with those who go heavily bent down by the load of their responsibility, whose saturnine ego considers itself indispensable and leaves nothing to God (the sun, the heart), and so denies itself the warmth of life and offers up love to duty.

Consider the flowers of this educative family — and note which bloom the earliest in the summer and which later: the more peaceful the soul situation, the later in the summer it blooms, i.e. the riper the sign of the Zodiac.

Lesser Foxglove

The lesser foxglove (*Gratio officinalis*) is rather more friendly. It too helps those who find no way of venting their feelings, and so are dropsical, and vexatious with jaundice — a Venus or Mars who cannot break out. The tea of this herb gives peace to those who cannot achieve a cure by themselves.

Speedwell

The speedwell (*Veronica officinalis*) has pretty blue flowers, opened up entirely to the sun, like the innocent eyes of children. But they quickly fall off (and that is why the Germans call the plant Männertreu — 'Men's faithfulness'). It cures a childlike person who cannot understand how her marriage could have gone so wrong — because she could not match up with her much deeper partner, and now she may suffer from tuberculosis, the consumption of an unhappy love, or perhaps only bronchitis, which is the beginning. Let her quickly drink tea of Veronica! Perhaps the sorrow expresses itself in asthma (inability to relax, through incomplete exhalation) or perhaps the poison of the soul has caused inflammation of the pelvis or eczema. For all these ailments, amongst young people and children in particular, speedwell is an excellent remedy.

Brooklime

The brooklime (*Veronica beccabunga*) is a close relative of the speedwell and lives by the waterside. It, too, cures the blockages of frustrated feelings: dropsy, eczema and congestion of the liver. It is rich in vitamin C, the vitamin of Venus!

Eyebright

Eyebright (*Euphrasia officinalis*) grows in grass and stealthily sucks a little life juices from the roots of other plants, even though it also make its own. Its purple and white striped flowers have two lips, but these are not pressed angrily together. It is a weeping flower, good for all those who seek a way out of love's sorrow through the eyes as the escape route (*emunctorium,* as Paracelsus called it) for the poison. Whoever cannot cry bitter tears suffers inflamed eyelids from the poison. (Inflammation comes from a frustrated Venus in a fire sign, while a swollen gland is associated with Venus in a water sign.) For all these ailments and for diabetes (Venus-Jupiter conflict) a tea can be made from eyebright and this can also be used, after it has been soaked through a cloth, for bathing the eyes — for really bright eyes!

Aaron's Rod

The mullein and the Aaron's rod, two kinds of Verbascum, rise up stately with open yellow flowers and felted leaves. The flowers can be infused in a mixed herbal tea for sore throat. The felted covering often indicates soothing.

22. Foxglove

(*Digitalis purpurea, lutea*)

It is June. I am sitting writing in my magic garden, with a row of profusely blooming rose bushes on the one side, pink and red against a background of dark trees. In front of me, against the little wall clad in dark-green cotoneaster, sheltered and quiet in the morning sun, are the serious purple flowery stalks of the foxglove. Like an upraised sceptre in the royal hand, it rises solemnly on its leaves, bearing long bells and, because of an inhibiting hormone, a bud still at its upper end. As the bottom flowers fade and drop off, so buds open up at the top, slowly coloured by the sun to a deep purple. Seven bells have opened simultaneously. Mysteriously, the honey markings on the pale base with dark red spots entice insects deep inside in order to drink from the nectar. They are mostly bumble bees, crawling into the bell with their fat hairy bodies, rubbing their brushes, probably laden with pollen from another flower, along the sticky stamen, which lies ready concealed against the upper edge of the bell.

The bumble bee fits the opening exactly; he is the special friend of the foxglove. Biologists have discovered that there is a bumble bee track across Europe, a strip where the foxglove runs riot in trees and gardens and where bumble bees are also the most prolific. No doubt, this is surmounted in the earth's crust and atmosphere by a so-called magnetic line, a certain vibration attuned to the same cosmic force as the bumble bee and foxglove.

Its Nature

In contemplating the foxglove, the first impression it makes is that of being turned inwards, the guardian of a great secret, namely that of its power, which must be used wisely. Touched any old how, the plant is toxic and so mothers warn their little ones against it — never stick your finger in one of the 'gloves'! However, the poison from the leaf, flower and seed can, when diluted, produce the heart medicine digitalis which is in fact prepared from the yellow-flowering variety. Its effect is to strengthen the heart and arteries and it is calming and a diuretic. The seats of ego, the heart and kidneys, are therefore involved. Do we not say "At heart, he is a . . ."? This plant therefore helps an ego to remain incarnated and so extends its earthly existence. Flowers in a vase stand longer with a little foxglove tea in the water. Saturn, the agent of both permanence and death, is the cosmic power manifested in this plant and in it, with each bell of the foxglove looking downwards, he expresses his serious involvement with matter.

It is a plant which needs silence and which certainly would not fit any busy patch. It seeks the shady woods of central Europe where it grants trees, particularly conifers, a longer life. But it also loves the lonely, sunny silence of islands. I remember one of the Scilly Isles, lying in the Atlantic Ocean off the south-west point of England, which was uninhabited and entirely covered with purple foxglove in the radiant sub-tropical sun.

The Gulf Stream gives this area the glow of warm summer and also a mild winter, so that daffodils already bloom in December.

Neighbouring Cornwall has the ruins of King Arthur's castle at Tintagel and innumerable menhirs and stone circles from the Celtic culture. On the Scillies, at the outer edge of the islands where the ocean waves break on the rocks in plumes of spray, the sea birds build their nests on the plundered graves of the Celtic kings. A seagull stands on each gravestone of rock as if, within it, there lives on the spirit of the ruler whose body rests in 'islands of the blessed in the west'.

Perhaps, like the Azores, Canary and Cape Verde islands, the Scillies are mountain tops left over from the sunken Atlantis. And the secrets that digitalis keeps may well be connected with the holy ceremonial once celebrated by the Druids in this now sealed-off past. The foxglove keeps the secrets of old Celtic Europe. It looks at us as if saying, "I know much, but will not betray my secret. I am waiting until the West returns from the error of its ways and again understands my language. In the meantime, I choose my dwelling place in the gardens of wise women and whisper my wisdom to them in moonlit nights."

23. Honeysuckle
(*Lonicera caprifolium*)

Honeysuckle is a shrub with flaccid branches which wind themselves around each other and around a support in the neighbourhood and so they are to be found as a pretty decoration on the small oaks on the heath. In spring, it opens its cream-pink flowers with long projecting stamens and on mild moon evenings pours forth a fascinating scent — a scent that awakens love, tenderness and affection. Like an eternal lover, it embraces its tree. And a symbol of love is what it is, an image of the everlasting bonds of love.

A Honeysuckle Ballad

There is a ballad — a lay — in old French about Tristan and Isolde, who loved each other like the honeysuckle does the hazelnut tree. Their hearts became inseparable after they had both drunk a love potion, yet they had to live apart, since Isolde was married to King Mark of Cornwall. Tristan was his nephew, whom he had sent as his representative to fetch his bride, Isolde of Ireland, with the golden hair. One warm evening on the boat they became thirsty and all the wine on board had been drunk, but someone found a small pitcher that had been overlooked. It was the love potion that Isolde's mother had given to her maid-in-waiting for the evening of Isolde's wedding to King Mark. When Tristan and Isolde drank a goblet of it together and looked into each other's eyes, their fate was sealed — they remained united in love until death. But what pain they had to suffer for it.

King Mark banned Tristan from his court at Tintagel and he went back to his place of birth in southern Wales. But driven by his longing, he returned to Cornwall and hid in a wood, spending his nights in the huts of the poor. From them he learned that King Mark was to give a feast at Tintagel which he would attend with his Queen Isolde. There was only one road that led there and this passed through the wood where Tristan was staying. Overjoyed, he cut a hazel twig into a four-sided stick in which he cut his name and which he planted in the middle of the sand track. This was a sign which Isolde knew and would be bound to notice.

While Tristan hid in the undergrowth, the procession approached and Isolde recognised the sign. She asked her retinue to leave and wait an hour, since she was tired and wanted to rest awhile. She then entered the wood with her faithful servant.

Here, Tristan was waiting! With deep joy they embraced each other. He told her how long he had been pining for her, that he could not live without her. They were like the hazelnut and the honeysuckle: intertwined, they could live an age but apart the hazel and the honeysuckle die.

So they spoke together and Isolde tried to persuade Tristan to make his peace with King Mark. Finally, they had to part and took their leave in tears.

Tristan went back to Wales in order to await Mark's pardon. As he tried to sing while playing on the harp, his sorrow expressed itself in a new song: the song of the honeysuckle, *Le lai du chevrefeuille*.

Homoeopathic Cure

The English herbalist Edward Bach steeped the fresh flowers of the honeysuckle in the water of a brook which he then used as a medicine for those who continue to hanker after a fine past and a lost love. The essence of this flower has a relaxing, antispasmodic effect. It clears over-abundance of emotion from the soul and, by analogy, an excess of wet from the body: it is sudorific, diuretic and expectorant and restores internal balance. The leaf strengthens and the bark cleans the blood, cures catarrh and drives water out in the form of urine and sweat. The root is used for a blue dye. Blue is the colour of woman, of faithfulness and distance.

Here we again see the homoeopathic principle: like cures like. The plant that embraces so tightly can also slacken the overtight bonds of love. Love that cannot express itself changes to poison in the veins: the toxin of Venus. Honeysuckle drives it out.

The essence of the flower, analogous to the essence of the emotions, returns these to the proper course. That is the secret of homoeopathy. The original pattern of harmony is restored through the effect of analogous forms in the other kingdoms of nature.

24. Nasturtium

(*Tropaeolum majus*)

As the name might suggest, this garden plant originates in the tropics, which is clear from its fiery colours and the enormous force of light and heat that it radiates. Its flowers have many colours, but all are positive yang tones: dark red, light red, deep yellow, orange, salmon, all beautifully contrasted by the black honey mark. The mysterious depths of its wide-open flower entice insects who are obliged to crawl deep within it, because the nectar is stored at the back of the flower in a long spore. Impatient animals or those whose tongues are too short for the correct path break in by biting a hole in the spore. So, also, do children, who suck the nectar from it! But the intention of the plant is that entry should be by the magic gate and that the pistil be pollinated at the same time.

Its Place in Nature

The pretty seeds taste pithy and have an exhilarating effect if a few are mixed in the salad in order to bring yin and yang in balance. Because of this taste and effect, they were grown as field crops in the past in such places as the Gooi in the Netherlands, where Eschscholtzia was also grown in fields. These flower lands — the local name 'flower road' is still a reminder — were a splendid sight.

Artist gardens with the wooden huts of painters and poets in the spinneys of dwarf oak and the smallholdings with small reed-thatched houses where painters had taken lodging were rich in nasturtium growing rampant in fences and hedges. They could be found growing by summerhouses and round the fruit trees they protected against the spider mite. They belonged to the poetic villages of central Holland at the birth of this century, when the wild rose still flowered there on the open heath and sandy roads were still to be found with the tracks of the milk carts which drove to and fro morning and evening in order to milk the cows.

The nasturtium belonged to this as an expression of the intensive emotional life of artists, mystics and world reformers who had come to set up their community of Internal Brotherhood. Winding paths led through the woods to secret huts where people would sit meditating, playing the piano or casting horoscopes. The path was known only to friends who went there by full moon or with a lantern for an evening and night philosophising together. Great loves were inspired and again painfully broken. People lived spontaneously and honestly, walked barefoot in sandals and baked their own bread or bought it from the community bakehouse, which still stands there. They lived for art, for self-expression, driven by the spirit, elect, blessed with love or unutterably grieving with the pains of the world. People lived — and could pay for their meal at the local hotel with a painting. In the small, shaded houses, overgrown with ivy, with the roof ridge still just peeping out, lived people of worth who were happy with their pump and oil lamp, in the peaceful light of which many a profound book has been written.

Since that time, the summers and people's hearts have cooled greatly, and the nasturtium has virtually disappeared from the gardens with few honey and bumble bees left to crawl into them. The painters who, fired by their colours, would place them on their canvas, have now gone.

The leaf of the nasturtium is round — a very rare form and the product of the so-called heat ether. The typical feature of this plant is in fact its great internal heat. In chemical terms, this is located in the benzyl mustard oil which also gives the leaf its sharp taste and the seeds their spicy flavour. A little of the leaf can be mixed in a salad which can be decorated with the flowers.

Medicinal Powers

The sharp mustard oil acts as an antibiotic on undesirable bacteria, moulds and viruses; chewing a leaf disinfects the mouth and throat. The German firm of Madaus prepares a medicine from nasturtium against afflictions of the lung, called Troma caps (capsules), derived from the Latin name of the plant, *Tropaeolum majus*. And the well-known Dr Vogel recommends nasturtium together with butterbur against emphysema of the lungs. The tincture of the fresh root expels hook worm. Nasturtium also features in Dr Vogel's herbal salt 'Herbamare'.

The plant contains not only benzyl mustard oil, abundant nitrogen and sulphur but also iodine, iron, phosphates and potash. Herb and seed have a warming, expectorant, cleansing effect, they promote menstruation and the release of urine and are rich in vitamin C (so important for the ingestion of calcium).

25. Vervain
(*Verbena officinalis*)

One of southern Europe's finest plants is the vervain which, although it occurs throughout Europe, deploys its greatest force when it absorbs the southern sun. It is a plant of Venus and Mercury, which likes to grow along hedges and walls, with long ears of small lilac flowers. The *Verbena odorata* variety smells lovely and it belongs to the family of *Verbenaceae*. In French it is called *verveine* and along the Riviera tea can be purchased of the dried herb, which retains its scent for a very long time.

It contains a special kind of tannin, iron and potassium and saponin. It should be collected in the dog days, i.e. at the end of August, in the last quarter of the moon, between the 23rd and 30th days of its course and, because it is a holy herb, a blessing should be uttered.

Ancient Uses

Hung about the neck when fresh it attracts love to anyone and drives off all pain. A bunch of the stalks and leaves placed on the head takes away all kinds of headache, whatever the cause. For men, it is a strong aphrodisiac producing large quantities of seed and brings prosperity to the house, field or vineyard where it grows. The herb should be worn when a tree is planted, when its powers will help its roots to become established.

Children who wear verbena round their necks behave properly and pleasantly, display a clear head and like learning. In days past the herb was hung by house doors in order to fend off evil spirits, disease and enchantment. For this purpose, the root can also be worn on a string around the neck. If the herb is placed in a dove-cot, all the doves in the neighbourhood will collect there; they love the scent and are associated with vervain in the way cats are attracted by valerian, catmint and chives. If a party is to be successful, wine infused with the fresh leaves of vervain should be sprinkled in the place where it is to be held.

This herb was renowned in antiquity and much used in religious ceremonies. The druids of the Celts used it when forecasting the future in the ether. The Romans used an infusion of verbena as holy water to clean their altars before the service was due to start. Emissaries who went to parley with the enemy wore vervain as a token of peaceful intentions. After all, it put them in a peace-loving mood.

The effects of vervain on the human body are multifarious and very powerful, according to tradition. Nervine, antispasmodic, febrifuge, hepatic, astringent, tonic, sudorific, diuretic, emollient, healing, cleansing and anodyne. Special applications are the following: ailments of the bronchial passages and coughing, particularly whooping cough, are helped by it. It improves the blood and all other vital juices. The powers of sight are strengthened by it appreciably.

Remedial Virtues

All ailments of the head, particularly colds, are cured by vervain, particularly if picked in the month of the Ram (21 March—20 April) which governs the head and belongs to Mars and iron. The fresh herb is placed on the forehead and temples. It frees a blocked liver, dissipates gallstones and cures jaundice, for which the whole plant must be boiled down. The plant is particularly useful for complaints of the spleen and against stitch in the side. Recipe: the leaves are chopped small and mixed with beaten egg white and rye flour and placed on cottonwool as a poultice on the sore spot. Otherwise, the leaves may be cooked with vinegar and then placed on it.

The fresh juice of the plant is used as an eye-wash and is taken to remove mucus or stone and against blood in the urine. It cures anaemia and pleurisy. On wounds and sores it promotes healing. Infections of the skin beneath the hair of the head are cured by it. It improves the circulation, particularly amongst old people. Used as a gargle, it cures infections of the throat and makes breath pleasant. Infused in warm honeyed water it is good for the bronchial passages.

Rheumatic pains are eased by a poultice of the leaves of verbena boiled in vinegar. A tea of verbena, shepherd's purse, red vine, cypress, myrtle and heath groundsel is invigorating for old people. It causes their blood to circulate better and helps them contain their urine. It is a specific for fistula in the anus and piles (as a poultice).

In all these applications the smoothing and accelerating effect of Mercury and the loving, healing and comforting effect of Venus can be clearly recognised. The most noble and really the most unique verbena is that which comes from South America and is grown in southern Europe for its enticing smell. The Italians call it *Limoncina* (the citron-scented: *Lippia citriodora Kunth*); it is also called *Aloysia citriodora* or *Verbena triphylla,* and, in English, herb Louisa. It improves the digestion, strengthens and calms the nerves, relaxes spasms, removes mucus from the bronchial passages and reduces fever. The true verbena oil is made from this plant. The tea of the plant can be simply drunk for pleasure!

26. Meadow Saffron
(*Colchicum autumnale*)

There are plants which break the rules and flower on the bare wood and show their leaves only when flowering has finished, for example the various kinds of ornamental cherries. There are also plants which, coming from the other hemisphere, complete their flowering in the autumn or winter, apparently against the season, such as the ivy. The plants that display both these alien habits together are rare. One such is the meadow saffron which flowers in the autumn as if unaware of time.

The meadow saffron (*Colchicum autumnale*) is seldom found in the fields of Britain and more commonly found throughout central Europe, for example in Switzerland, where it dots the pastures with lilac in September. In Britain, another kind of Colchicum is more common, which is very similar and is sold in the market as a bulb that blooms without water. This plant, too, has a lilac flower very similar to the crocus, with its stem proceeding directly from the bulb. You just place it on the window ledge and it flowers, providing everything it needs for itself.

The Life-Cycle of Meadow Saffron

During flowering, the beginnings of the fruit and the stem of the plant and its leaves are still being composed, shapeless, deep within the bulb. When flowering has finished, the plant develops these components in secrecy during the winter. The stamen, consisting of three pistils, has a stem of 15 to 20 cm in length and the pollen must travel down quite a distance in order to reach the embryo fruit in May. In the meantime the stalk has begun to grow in April and has sprouted long, narrow leaves. The seed ripens only late in spring. Then, all parts of the plant above ground die away. The meadow saffron therefore plays at winter in mid-summer. In the autumn, then, the naked flowers appear, hence the country name in England 'naked ladies' and the Italian *Dama nuda*.

Properties

We can see that the life forces work tardily in this plant, therefore. It is poisonous to human and animal, hence the French name 'tue-chien', 'kill-the-dog', and paralyses the central nervous system. In ancient times it was called *Hermodactylon*, after the god and planet force Hermes (Mercury) who drives the electrical nerve currents upwards through the spinal cavity in order to feed the brain.

Although the plant is poisonous, the seed has traditionally been used to prepare a tincture or an infusion in wine of which not more than 1 g a day could be taken. Against what? Against the old-fashioned complaint of gout or 'podagra', a kind of inflammation resulting, in men, from sexual excess.

In other words,

> *Bacchus the father, Venus the mother,*
> *Coena the midwife, faciunt podagra!*

Thus runs an old rhyme:

> *Wine and women and eating late*
> *make podagra!*

Nowadays, Colchicum D3 and above (i.e. diluted at least 1000 times) is made in homoeopathy against rheumatism, rheumatic endocarditis, goitre and enteritis. This medicine is prepared from the bulb. The Colchicum toxin also acts on the muscular tissue, and the mucous membrane covering of the joints and periosteum. It has also been found that the poison of the meadow saffron prevents the halving of the number of chromosomes in the production of new life. It is used in agriculture and stock breeding to produce giant forms, giant grain, giant cabbages, giant rabbits. The grains obtained in this way are much larger than normal but are certainly not twice as nutritious, so that as a result the farmer becomes rich and the consumer is cheated. It seems that this plant excites lust and avarice in humans.

However, understanding that evil is only good compacted too greatly, and poison therefore no more than over-concentrated medicine, we can by dilution change these apparent evils into a blessing for humankind. Thus, the satanic wilfulness of the meadow saffron is refined to a medicine for self-made ill which is no more than a disturbance of the balance.

27. Cashew Nut Tree

(*Anacardium*)

There are two varieties of the Anacardium tree: the western and the eastern. The western (*Anacardium occidentale*) grows in the Americas, in such places as the Dutch West Indies. This tree produces the curved cashew nuts which are very nutritious and healthy. The unroasted type are obtainable in health stores. In the country of origin, they are eaten as a medicine against stomach and duodenal ulcers. The root is a medicine against severe diarrhoea, the bark against fever and the skin of the fruit, used externally, against warts and corns. The tart, black juice of the skin of the fruit is used as marking ink and contains the irritant substance cardol.

The *Anacardium orientale* (or *Semicarpas orientales*) comes from the East Indies. Its English name is the 'kidney bean' because the shape of the nut is similar to that of the kidney. The fruit sits at the top of a swollen flower base.

A homoeopathic medicine is prepared from this fruit: Anacardium D3 to D6, used against stomach or duodenal ulcer, when this is characterised by pains in an empty stomach. It is also used against paralysis of the rectum, whereby the stool cannot be expelled. The sufferer feels that there is a lump somewhere in his body. Another characteristic pointing to this medicine is a feeling as if an external part of the body, for example a finger, has been cordoned off by a band.

In high dilutions, this homoeopathic substance is used against shingles, nettle rash and eczema with itching and blistering. And also against exhaustion, over-stress and loss of memory. It is remarkable that patients to whom this is given say they have 'two wills', seeking to fulfil contrary purposes. The one will is felt as one's own, the other as an outside one, against which no headway can be made. This may be an invisible being by whom the patient is possessed; it can also be the will of a person close by who threatens to dominate the patient. Characteristically the subject tends to swear, in order to drive off the overbearing force. Anacardium D30 is then the means of freeing the patient from this force. (Another substance is Lycopodium D12.) In addition, the patient should eat cashew nuts!

Further, incense herbs are useful for purifying the air and ether: needles of the pine or juniper, sage, rosemary, spearmint, peppermint, lavender, rue, root of valerian, blessed thistle, marjoram, coriander seed, camomile and sweet basil. The dried herbs are placed on a tin plate on the stove or on glowing charcoal. At the same time, the threatened person may be given the tea of the plant to drink.

28. The Walnut Tree
(*Juglans regia*)

The walnut tree with its large nuts is a tree of Jupiter which occurs in central Europe, in Greece and Asia Minor, Persia, Kashmir, the Himalayas and China. It produces catkins that fall in the spring and the walnuts ripen in the autumn as seeds within thick green bolsters. When cut through, these produce a juice with a brown stain used to dye hair. It is difficult to remove from the hands but the trouble is worthwhile — the fresh nut has a deliciously soft white flesh and is something of a delicacy.

Brain Tonic

The kernel has the shape of the human brain, complete with the division to left and right. According to the doctrine of signatures, the walnut must therefore be the right food for the brain, and this is a fact. People who do much mental work should eat plenty of them. Since the damp young nuts cannot be kept long without becoming mildewed, the trade stores them in sulphur, in the course of which they become steadily drier and less tasty through the winter. They contain oil and resin and are very nutritious. The felty pith is infused in boiling water as a tea against high blood pressure. The thick peel contains vitamin C in abundance and can be used (externally) as a styptic. Since the walnut is a brain tonic, it retains the human ego within the pole of thought in the head, even when much alcohol is drunk (which does the reverse). This reverses the human organism so that the pole of life and the subconscious part of the soul gain the upper hand, bringing the hidden truths to light in the inebriate.

It has been proved that walnuts keep people sober even when large quantities of wine are drunk. At the time when Austria formed part of the Roman Empire — under the name Noricum — the Roman Emperor Marcus Aurelius Probus (278-282) had vineyards built for his soldiers in the foothills of the Alps since the spring water was difficult to reach in the jungles which then existed. However, when drunk, the soldiers fought so much amongst themselves that great numbers were killed. The Emperor thereupon had nut trees planted all over amongst the vineyards. A wine still exists called *Nussberger* after the nut-hill on which it grows. Every wine shop had to offer nuts free of charge with the wine and, in this way, drunkenness disappeared, together with its consequences. This habit still exists—at the *Heckenwrite* where people can sit and drink wine outdoors in the autumn, plates of nuts are placed ready on the tables. And so larger quantities are always drunk!

Healing Powers

It is not surprising that a tree of Jupiter (Zeus) should bestow both intelligence and healing power. The goddess Pallas Athene, who ruled over the arts of war and science, was born from the head of Zeus. The thinking of Jupiter — judgement and ethics — are, of course, seated in the human forehead.

The nut tree's healing powers are great. Both the leaves and the nuts are astringent and clean the intestines. The tannic acid in the leaves ensures that an infusion of them, when applied both internally and externally, is very suitable for the lymphatic type of person, in whom mucus and other fluids tend to pile up and whose glands therefore are quick to swell up through an excess of fluid, for example scrofulous children and women who suffer from leucorrhoea and inflammation of the womb. For a good hip bath, take two handfuls of fresh leaves to a litre of water, though much less of the dried variety, and allow them to infuse for a quarter of an hour. Mix this with cold water up to the desired temperature and let the leaves remain in the bath. The tea of the nut tree leaf, when drunk with meals, cures diabetes, eczema and impetigo and expels intestinal worms. Infused in combination with yarrow and gentian it produces an effective tea against piles.

The juice of the green peel, traditionally known as *Rob nucum*, when pressed out and allowed to thicken, cures sore throats and inflammation of the uvula and tonsils.

The oil pressed from walnuts, and kept at least a year (since it is the better the longer it is kept), removes gravel in the kidney if given in an enema. The oil can be effectively applied to burns together with chalk water. Boiled in wine, it cures sores. The roasted nutshells mixed with wine produce a potion against loss of hair. The catkins, like those of the hazelnut, are a strong sudorific and are infused as a tea for 'fluey' people in the early spring.

It is an outstanding tree which cannot tolerate oaks and small brush in its vicinity and requires good soil and a mild climate; it does not like frost. Its wood is highly prized for fine furniture.

Anyone with a nut tree in their garden is bound to come under its beneficial influence. It also imparts steadiness and self-confidence to the human soul so that we feel capable of tackling the problems of life through the powers of the mind. Jupiter, after whom the tree is named — *Ju-glans regia* = royal gland of Jupiter — grants faith and a positive attitude to life.

PART 3
Meditation

Find a restful spot by an open window without draughts, preferably near a wood or coal fire. If possible, sit near your own altar,
with flowers, a bowl of water, precious stones and two candles
burning in copper candlesticks.

Take off your shoes and anything that may get in the way, shake
your head and shoulders and relax your arms and legs. Draw a
deep breath three times and heave a deep sigh. Now sit on the
ground with legs crossed, easy and relaxed. The arms resting on
the folded legs, the hands hanging loosely down or lying with their
palms upwards. The following words are then spoken or thought
— or, perhaps, played on a tape recorder.

The object is to feel, live and be what is spoken.

I Am a Water-Lily

I am a water-lily in bud. Earth and water support me.
The wind rocks me.
Now I feel the warm sun above me — I breathe it in
 — I shall unfold!
My golden heart swells. My white petals open, one by one.
The sky is roundabout me like a blue bell.
I am at the centre of it.
My heart beams in the sun love. We are one.
I am the warm light. *Nothing* can happen to me!
Now a force pulses upwards through my cool stalk—
I laugh, I sing to myself. Joy buzzes roundabout me:
butterflies, dragonflies and bees. My pond reflects the sky.
Happiness is all that exists.
If I now get up and go I shall remain the water-lily.
I shall be carried on heaven-reflecting water.
My open heart bathes in the imperishable light.

Now the meditation comes to a close, as you close yourself by thinking of a golden circle around you. The candles are extinguished but the light in the heart still burns.

Farewell of a Beech Leaf

My days are numbered —
for three nights no further sap has flowed to me
from mother tree —
I am drying out and feel parched —
My stalk is withering away —
I must take my farewell.
I still remember how I awakened in a far-off spring night —
I lay, rolled together, folded up, in my pointed bud.
It became warmer roundabout,
I felt a need to stretch — snap!
A bud-scale broke open —
I felt an urge to wriggle loose — my cap fell off —
I smelled the sweet smell of spring rain, a drop fell on my top —
it was as if I woke with a fright — I turned further out of the fold
— again a scale fell off, and yet another — and — I was free — and
breathed — so I stayed listening to the rushing rain, the whole
night through.
It became light. I saw the wood. And all my sisters who had wriggled loose during that night. Silent and astonished we felt the sunlight shine over us, like a caress. One by one we straightened the
pleats in our dress. Very light-green it was then, and soft, full of
fine hairs. The sun shone warmer and warmer and we felt ourselves becoming stronger and stronger!
Voices beneath us said: Look! Here is a beech in leaf!
Proudly, I spread myself out yet more smoothly.
How lovely were those spring days!
The sun turned my colour from green to green.
I became stronger and more serious.
Birds chattered to each other in the branches. I learned much. By
day it was work. Sunlight and water laboured in us and I just
breathed.
The air was not always fine.
Sometimes it was dirty and foul.

Then I closed my mouths and allowed myself to hang limp.

But then mother's voice penetrated through to me:

Children! Do not give up!

We are here to fetch the dirt from the air!

We keep the wood fresh and clean

For our friends, the birds, the squirrels and the rabbits and in fact the people too.

So we did our best: all five thousand sisters on our mother-tree and all the leaves on neighbouring trees, throughout the wood.

Oh, those summer nights — the face of the moon, rising great and friendly, orange above the heath's edge — and a whispering ran through the wood — very silently we spread ourselves out.

Then we saw the rows of elves free themselves from the veils of mist on the heath and dance in the moonlight.

Silently we watched till the moon disappeared — and behind the wood, in red-golden glow, the sun appeared, surrounded by bird-song — and we shook along in a flurry of joy!

Now that is past. The birds have become silent. Many have gone. Now the morning light comes slowly — in a chill mist, in which the wood-pigeons wing noiselessly, grey in the white shroud of the mist.

I feel that I am changing.

I have seen the beechnuts ripen — now their houses spring open and tick, tick, the nuts fall and cover the woodland ground. Busily the squirrels scurry around.

Mother is finished with her work for this year.

I now feel weak and yellow. What has happened to my green colour?

The weak sun brings no succour, but enchants my dress: it becomes dry and sere and then gold — Oh, gold like the summer sun!

When I see her in the blue autumn air, I thank her: Oh, to be allowed to go, gold like the sun!

Now I feel my time has come. I rattle from dryness when the wind passes by.

My stem will not hold.

Goodbye mother tree — I am going — I shall fall on the moss and change slowly into earth. The wind will catch me up and lay me down again — but I shall know nothing because I am going to sleep.

Sleep as I slept in the bud.
The mist comes up. When now the night wind rocks me
I shall let my stalk go.
Mother — farewell!

PART 4
Trees and Humans

Trees and humans both stand like twin-poled beings set up between earth and sun. The trunk of the tree and the human trunk stretch out by day, attracted in the one direction by the force of gravity and in the other by the sun. The constructive forces of the earth rise within the inner sap channels of the tree and through the left-hand stream in the spinal canal, while at the top, leaf and lungs absorb energy from sun and air and, converting it to food, distribute it to all the organs along the outer sap channels and down the right-hand, spinal stream, storing whatever remains. In the morning, everything rises up and in the afternoon moves down, a giving and taking, extrovert and introvert, aligned with the sun.

Condensation and scent in the tree are at their peak at the end of the morning, the great giving. So, humans give their heart and spirit to their work in the morning. Both use power and become more slender as a result.

In the afternoon, the tree expands with the food it has prepared and the human soul is full, enriched with impressions that must now be processed during evening contemplation: the great taking.

Between roots and crown the trunk branches out into lateral branches; and in humans, sets of nerves spring from the spinal marrow.

In the tree, reciprocation between root and crown is perfect. Its branches spread out equidistant with its roots. In humans, balance and cooperation between the poles is frequently dislocated: first, they exhaust their pole of thought in studying for examinations or intellectual work, so that they close off the supply of life force, and then they shut down their moral awareness. Human beings therefore benefit greatly from contemplating the life of the tree, so that the tree within themselves becomes healthier and stronger.

Tree Meditation

Stand up straight and free, with feet slightly apart, planted sturdily on the ground (no heels, or low heels, no rubber soles), the arms stretched out diagonally with widespread fingers, like branches with leaves; the eyes closed for concentration. While the leader speaks the words (if you are alone, you can speak them or think them yourself, or, if necessary, record them and play them back). Enter into the essence of the tree — become a tree.

I am a tree. My roots reach deep into the earth and suck up its nutrient forces, I feel them rise within me. How surely and safely I stand anchored to Mother Earth.

An early morning wind makes my branches move and rocks the nests of the birds. Small sounds awake. A cock crows in the distance.

My favourite bird flies from its nest to my top — a joyful cry greets the streak of dawn appearing on the horizon.

Now the others join in, rejoicing. I bear their choir on my branches and drink in the glow that rises in the east. The sun appears: the sun! Its fiery face rises up, pink and orange, and my sap hurries to meet it, my leaves rise up, it makes me tingle!

The sun greets me and my fellows by our name and we greet it in turn. The birds rejoice — the sun's power fills the air like organ music. My leaves now breathe and work, making their green leaf pulp and food for all my body from sunlight and carbon.

Luckily, I stand in the force field between earth's support and sun's blessing. It is my salvation. The mist elves have fled upwards along my trunk; it becomes warm beneath; the beetles swarm over my trunk; the bees buzz in, my blossoms open and begin to converse with them.

I send out my scent for the whole of this good earth, basking in the sun's heat.

It makes me sleepy. It is past midday. My branches and leaves weaken (*arms drop*). I am full. Now my nutritious sap runs down along the leaf nerves, the stem, the twig, into my trunk through my strong branches, and each cell drinks from it.

The sun begins to set but leaves its fire within me. My birds fly back to their nests. A cool breeze whispers its evening greeting through my branches. The sun takes its leave in its grand evening gold — and now is gone. Closing myself up, I feel the damp mist on my feet.

Daylight creeps away and the dear moon rises in stately quiet. But I cannot rest: I must feed my cambium, which builds new cells, build up stock, carry out repairs, discard used-up tissue for small animals. I look inwards to my life-business and descend with my sap into my roots. Stars twinkle. And I can feel my branches spreading out in order to bear those golden fruits while my root-hairs feel and feel — everything whispered throughout the earthly globe (*spread arms and legs in an X-shape*). I am the All and the All flows through me. I am the world-tree Yggdrasil.

Tomorrow, I shall shrink back to one tree in the wood doing the work of taking, converting and giving — a tree which, growing from sun and earth, protects, feeds and delights plants and elves, animals and people. Deep in my inmost core I shall continue to know, even though I may grow a thousand years, and I bear the All in me, enfolded by day, unfolded by night. I am Yggdrasil. I, tree, am All.

God created humans in his own image. This image or cosmic pattern is an organism consisting of two poles linked by a circuit of forces. So God and humans as poles together form a living organism, as do sun and planet, life and thought. So the microcosm is created in the same pattern as the macrocosm.

The Tree of Life — *Yggdrasil: the I-bearer*

In the Norse myth (Edda) this pattern was represented as a tree, the tree of life or world-ash. An eagle nests in its three branches which support the heavenly vault and carry the stars like gold fruits. Its three roots embrace the underworld, a spring of water lying by each. At the foot of the trunk, near the spring of Hvergelmir, the dragon Nidhoggr has its home; it gnaws at the root, to prevent the sap rising through the trunk and so to let the crown wither. The squirrel Ratatoskr bounds up and down the trunk, gossips with the eagle about the dragon (or snake) and with the dragon about the eagle. Sweet honeydew drips down from the branches into the three springs.

By the spring of Urd live the three fates or Nornes: Urd, who starts spinning the life-thread of humans, Werdandi, who weaves two life-threads into one at the wedding and Skuld (guilt, karma) who cuts the thread at death. The three of them guard their holy golden spring, where two swans swim.

The spring of Mimir lies right beneath the trunk and grants wisdom. It is not difficult to penetrate these symbols: the squirrel (Mercury, Odin, Wodan) maintains the circulation between the poles, especially the rising stream, while the falling stream is indicated by the honeydew dropping down. In the human body, the trunk is the spinal column, the circulation passing along the blood and nerve courses and along the meridians of the body in life.

The crown with sparkling star-fruits (imitated by us as a Christmas tree with lights and gleaming baubles) or richly foliated (the may tree or maypole with its wreath of green and flowers) is represented in the human head by the branching of the nerves of the brain, along which electric sparks flash when 'we see the light'. Every branch can also be regarded as an indication of an important bundle of nerves (plexus) proceeding from the endocrine gland and chakram: the thyroid gland in the throat, the pituitary (hypophysis) lower in the head, lying by the point at the nose root, and the pineal body higher in the head, associated with the crown chakram, where awareness of inside and outside, of beneath (the body and the so-called subconscious of the vegetative nerve system) and above (conscious observance and knowledge, and inspiration) meet at one point as all-knowledge.

The three roots and springs similarly indicate centres, this time in the lower body, a plexus, a gland and a chakram. By Urd lie the sex glands (the two swans are ovaries or testicles), the sacral plexus, the sacrum and the tail chakram, where the pure, neutral cosmic creative force enters to be transformed into three phases. Each has the choice either to produce outwardly as a sexual force or to refine itself further until it rises as an ethereal hormone force and nutrient sap, through the trunk, to the pole of thought where it develops the soul. Here, therefore, indeed lies the source of human life, outward (procreation) and inward. Here the moon and Venus reside.

The spring of Hvergelmir lies by the prostate gland, the plexus prostaticus, and the pubis (because here desire commences, portrayed in Nidhoggr) and is also connected with the adrenal glands. Here Mars, the aggressive sexual ego, resides.

By the spring of Mimir (memory) lies the solar plexus and liver, where Mars (preparation of gall) and Jupiter keep house together with the 'alchemists'. This is the home of dream or subconsciousness, the kitchen hearth of the fairy tale, because here Jupiter is busy and can convert albumen, sugar and fat into each other as required in his alchemist's oven.

Beneath and above correspond with each other (Ratatoskr): the sex glands with the thyroid, the liver with the eyes, brains and pituitary, the prostate plexus and adrenal glands with the hypophysis, and each of them with reciprocal effect.

Caduceus

In the Greek myth, the tree of life is called the staff of Mercury (Hermes) or Caduceus, which Mercury received from Apollo, the sun god. This staff is wreathed with two snakes wound three and a half times, while above their heads two wings sprout from the staff and its top is crowned with an acorn. This is quite clear: the snakes form the circulation, the upward (left) and downward streams passing through ganglia on either side of the spinal cord and possibly through the life-body. The wings relate to the lungs and the acorn to the pituitary (hypophysis). The one stream (yin) represents the stream of impressions conveyed to the brain from outside with the aid of the senses, while the downward stream gives commands, transmitting awareness to the muscles as a conscious reaction to those impressions.

However, the two streams do not always pass through the consciousness. If a specific impression is always followed by one and the same command, the path is shortened, by-passing consciousness; if the stimulus from outside arrives in the extension of the column, in the neck (the medulla oblongata, seat of the moon), it will then connect up with the outgoing stream which will attach the same muscle command as always. This is the origin of automatic actions, fixed habits, good manners and training: everything we need not think about twice. The vegetative nervous system and the subconscious in this way takes over a great deal of work from the central nervous system and the conscious. In this instance, the snakes' heads touch.

The disadvantage, however, is that the pineal body no longer receives the messages from beneath. All-knowledge is lost and the individual no longer knows what is happening in their body or in a large part of their soul. This is why science today no longer sees much purpose in this gland. Humans have become unknowing and helpless through this division into two separately operating systems, the cerebrum and cerebellum (with the extension of the spinal column), super- and subconscious.

It was not always so: once upon a time the full stream of consciousness would ride from the bottom up to the top: then, we knew everything we had to know and required no teachers, books or schools.

This is still always the case in the newly born child. It is still at one with everything — in paradise.

Biblical Symbols

In the Bible, this is described in Genesis. In paradise, there was a tree of life and a tree of knowledge. Humans ate the fruit of the tree of life (subconscious knowledge) and were without problems. Human beings were tempted, however, not only to become conscious and to become creative partners with God, but also to set up their own order. They no longer allowed the juices to rise up to the crown of their tree of life but began partly to reverse them halfway along their path and partly to tap them below at the pole of life in sexual exchange and material procreation. Nidhoggr chewed at the root. The crown withered: thought was no longer creative, the light of insight dimmed and nothing was left but rational casual reasoning in endless logic equations, as mechanical as a computer.

Only the three norms — past, present and future — determined thought, and so concepts arose of cause and effect (karma), sin, guilt and punishment, time and space, and all the sets of contrasts: good and evil, male and female, yang and yin, super- and subconsciousness. Humans became split, one-sided, helpless and abandoned beings through their knowledge of good and evil, living in a duality. The eagle of the spirit could no longer find a home in the withered branches, Ratatoskr no longer reached the top, the dragon governed humankind. That was the fall in Eden. The tree of life is changed into the tree of knowledge.

The Cross

When Roman Catholics cross themselves, they use the Jupiter and Saturn fingers first to point to the head, the Eagle (as the Scorpion is called in the East), then the solar plexus, the Bull, then the heart on the left, the Lion, and after that, on the right, the lungs, the Water Carrier (an air sign). These are the four Signs of the Fixed Cross, which are also combined with the four Evangelists, Matthew, Luke, Mark and John (the angel) respectively, the four figures that can be seen portrayed on copper bells. The pole of thought, the pole of life and the circulatory system (blood circulation and breathing) are therefore pointed to, and, at the same time, the four elements: water, earth, fire and air.

Golgotha

In the story of the crucifixion at Golgotha (i.e. the place of the skull) this event is portrayed as the possible redemption from sin (the second phase). The three crosses on the extension of the backbone are the ends of the caduceus itself, the central channel (Jesus Christ) and, next to him, those of the two streams, represented as thieves because they steal the light of consciousness from the pole of thought by immediately conveying the upward stream back downwards, to dark Egypt (which is the name given to the body in the gnostic texts).

If, therefore, the upward stream no longer lets itself be tempted in this direction but continues onwards to the top, to the consciousness in the cerebrum and, eventually, to the pineal body (at the top of the caduceus), then the thief will directly return to paradise with Christ, the central stream, as Jesus promised him, because all-knowledge is now restored and once returned gives unity to consciousness.

Then the eye of the spirit (represented as an eye in a triangle) will again open so that the essence of things will always be seen beyond their apparent forms. And then the split is healed at every level, there will be no sexual desire, and no further procreation will be required, because human beings will become refined and will no longer die. All force will now proceed upwards untapped through the central channel and the crown of the tree of life will again become green and sap-laden and the flowers of full thought (thought in analogies) will develop and produce the golden apples of wisdom. Nidhoggr has been overcome and the eagle will live at the top of the human for good.

The narthex stalk (the spinal column) in which Prometheus brought the fire of the gods to humankind then conveys this force according to the original intent. Prometheus, the striving human of the second phase, is unbound!

The snake on the caduceus then spits in the bowl — the grail of the human head — which receives inspiration as the end-product of all movement through the All.

Each one of us carries the tree of life within us and we can ourself decide whether we will let our crown be sere and dead or fresh, blooming and fruitful.

Index

More books from Altea Publishing

KARMAPA *Ken Holmes*

Many people have heard of the Dalai Lama, but fewer are aware of the Gyalwa Karmapa, Tibet's very first 'reincarnate' lama, who in June 1985 took birth again for the 17th time in this millennium among the nomads of Eastern Tibet. Drawing on a quarter-century of experience close to the senior lamas of the Kagyu tradition, including the 16th Karmapa, Ken Holmes not only tells the fascinating story of the finding of the new Karmapa but also presents information on topics such as the Karmapa's uniqueness, his lineage, reincarnation, the land of Tibet and Tibetan Buddhism itself — particularly that branch of it that the Karmapa embodies so perfectly — in the hope that it will help those who meet the Karmapa to gain more benefit from their experience and others to discover someone who will doubtless be an important figure in the coming century.

Pbk   ISBN 0 9524555 4 4   £12.95   168 pp   Illustrated

THE CALL OF PACAL VOTAN
Time is the Fourth Dimension *José Argüelles*

José Argüelles has for many years been exploring the Mayan concept of time based on his research into the mysteries of Palenque in Mexico and especially the lid of Pacal Votan's tomb. Part of his work has been to develop a fully usable Mayan-style 13-moon calendar, and the Dreamspell and Telektonon kits, which are multi-dimensional tools to help us walk the true time trail.

The Call of Pacal Votan serves both as a fascinating insight into the realm of time as the fourth dimension and as an advanced, detailed primer to accompany the study of the Dreamspell kit. The Mayan cosmological perspective is much more profound than our traditional Western view and in this book José Argüelles sets out the theoretical foundations necessary to understand it.

Pbk   ISBN 0 9524555 6 0   £11.95   144 pp

GALACTIC HUMAN HANDBOOK — ENTERING THE NEW TIME *Sheldon Nidle & José Argüelles*

Following the success of *You Are Becoming a Galactic Human* Sheldon Nidle presents timely information on the creation of Planetary Advocate Groups, which act as champions for planet Earth, the Spiritual Hierarchy and the Galactic Federation, and as nodes of consciousness for the next phase of activation of the planetary web of light. In the second part of the book, peace pilgrim and acclaimed author of *The Mayan Factor* José Argüelles presents evidence for the urgent need to move into a new timing frequency based on the Mayan 13-moon calendar approach. Both authors lecture extensively and through Operation Victory and VictoryNet are involved in creating a new network of light and educational tools dedicated to bringing about galactic culture through group work.

Pbk   ISBN 0 9524555 5 2   £11.95   158 pp + 18-page 'Resources' section

GEMS OF DHARMA, JEWELS OF FREEDOM
Tr. Ken & Katia Holmes

A new, authoritative translation of the great Tibetan Buddhist classic the *Dagpo Tarjen* by Jé Gampopa. For some 800 years this masterly overview of the Buddha's teaching has served as a handbook for followers of the twelve Kagyü traditions. Placing the quintessential meaning of hundreds of Buddhist scriptures in the palm of one's hand, it provides an ideal resource for those new to Buddhism and is an invaluable reference work for experienced practitioners.

Pbk   ISBN 0 9524555 0 1   £12.50   Hdbk   ISBN 0 9524555 1 X   £17.50
352 pp

TRANQUIL MIND   *Rob Nairn*

A simple, comprehensive introduction to Buddhism and meditation outlining the principles of this spiritual path in everyday language. The Buddha's teaching of impartiality, tolerance and respect for all religions emphasises the importance of meditation for developing inner peace, compassion and wisdom. Western meditators encounter unique problems caused by their cultural, social and psychological backgrounds. Drawing on his extensive academic and practical experience, the author introduces the subject in a manner which takes account of these influences.

Pbk   ISBN 1 874952 06 X   £5   62 pp

Ordering Information
The above may be ordered from the publisher. 10% discount on orders of 5 books or more, 25% discount on 10 or more, 35% discount on orders over £200. Add postage & packing charge: UK/EEC — £1.50 per book (up to maximum of £4.50). Rest of world — charged at cost. Please indicate if airmail required.
Please enclose payment with order. All non-UK orders payable by credit card only. Send to Altea Publishing, Parkmount House, 10 St Leonards Road, Forres IV36 0DW, Scotland. Tel/fax +44 (0)1309 673312